Missouri Orchids

by Bill Summers

Missouri Department of Conservation
Natural History Series, No. 1

Joan McKee • editor

**Dedicated to Julian Steyermark,
the master of Missouri's flora**

Third Edition
© copyright 1981, 1987, 1996
by the Conservation Commission of the State of Missouri
ISBN 1-887247-04-1

Introduction

The orchid family may be the largest flowering plant family in the world. Most of the more than 15,000 species are found in the tropics, but orchids also grow in bogs, meadows and woodlands across North America. Some are as striking as their tropical counterparts. Others have inconspicuous greenish flowers and may easily be overlooked in the field.

Orchids are a highly diverse group, although all species exhibit certain unique, easily seen characteristics. Orchids are monocots and, as such, share certain characteristics with other groups, such as lilies and grasses. Monocots are a group of plants characterized by leaves with parallel veins and flowers with three petals and three sepals. Orchid flowers differ from those of other monocots in having bilateral symmetry; that is, the right and left sides of the flower are mirror images of each other, like the human body. Many other monocots exhibit radial symmetry, like a circle. In orchid flowers, one petal differs markedly from the other two in size, shape or color. This petal, usually the lowermost one, is called the "lip."

Orchids generally do not have a separate pistil and stamens; in orchids, the stigma, style and one or more stamens join to form a column, which is often brightly colored and petallike. All orchids have inferior ovaries, meaning that the sepals and petals are attached above the ovary. Each ovary contains many minute ovules that develop into tiny seeds when fertilized.

Most orchids exhibit one other unique characteristic. The orchid flowers twist on their stalk during development, so that the lip, which was originally the uppermost petal, becomes the lowermost petal. In several of our native species, this twisting occurs incompletely or not at all, so the lip orients to the side or top of the flower.

The lower petal, or lip, is the most conspicuous part of the orchid flower. It is usually larger and more brightly colored than the other petals and the sepals, which are often similar in color and shape and are inconspicuous. Frequently, the uppermost sepal and lateral petals are joined or converge to form a hood over the lip.

There are 35 species of orchids, representing 16 genera, in Missouri. All are native, with the exception of *Epipactis helleborine,* which was introduced from Europe. No orchids in Missouri are common in the

3

sense that we think of other plants, such as black-eyed Susans or even bluebells, as being common. Yellow lady-slippers are fairly common for orchids, yet many people will never see one growing naturally.

Because orchids tend to be fairly sensitive to habitat disturbance, many species are reduced in number as a result of pressures exerted on their environment by man. Sixteen of Missouri's 35 orchid species are listed in the *Rare and Endangered Species Checklist of Missouri*. Because the status of listed species changes periodically, it is suggested that those who desire the current status refer to the most recent list, which is available from the Missouri Department of Conservation. The following species are presently of conservation concern in the state:

Scientific name	Common name
Cypripedium candidum	Small white lady-slipper
Cypripedium reginae	Showy lady-slipper
Isotria medeoloides	Small whorled pogonia
Isotria verticillata	Large whorled pogonia
Liparis loeselii	Loesel's twayblade
Malaxis unifolia	Green adder's mouth
Platanthera ciliaris	Yellow fringed orchid
Platanthera clavellata	Green wood orchid
Platanthera flava	Pale green orchid
Platanthera leucophaea	Eastern prairie fringed orchid
Platanthera praeclara	Western prairie fringed orchid
Pogonia ophioglossoides	Snake mouth
Spiranthes lacera (var. *gracilis* only)	Slender ladies' tresses
Spiranthes lucida	Shining ladies' tresses
Spiranthes ovalis	Oval ladies' tresses
Tipularia discolor	Cranefly orchid

All of our orchids should be treated with care and protected so their beauty may be enjoyed in generations to come. Most orchids are specific in their habitat requirements and will not tolerate disturbance. In addition, all orchids require a mycorrhizal association to obtain the nutrients they need from the soil. In a mycorrhizal association, the threads of a fungus are attached to the roots of a plant. Without the fungus, orchids would not be able to absorb the soil's nutrients. When an orchid plant is dug, the association is usually damaged and the plant does not survive when transplanted. Some orchids no longer possess chlorophyll and depend upon these fungi that live in the soil for all their food. These are known as saprophytic species. Orchids, especially rare ones, should be enjoyed in their natural habitat and transplanted only when their habitat is destroyed.

Acknowledgments

I welcome this opportunity to express my gratitude to John E. Wylie, former Natural History officer of the Missouri Department of Conservation, for his devoted interest in this project and the promotion of this publication. I am especially indebted to Virginia K. Wallace, who acted as technical editor on the first edition and did much to prepare the manuscript. George Yatskievych, with whom I have worked for several years on the Flora of Missouri Project, helped with the present edition. I also am grateful to Bernadette Dryden, June Hunzeker and Joan McKee for their work editing the three editions of this book.

Members of the botany group of the Webster Groves Nature Study Society and the Missouri Native Plant Society were helpful in providing information and making comments. The following people were especially helpful: the late Art Christ, who made available for study his private herbarium, which is now at the Missouri Botanical Garden; Father James Sullivan; Betty Nellums; Nell Menke; Karen Haller; John Krebs; Steve Orzell; John Molyneaux; and Mary Wiese.

My thanks also to Gregg Iffrig, Dr. Leo Galloway and Larry Maher, who supplied information on *Platanthera praeclara,* and to Mark Pelton, Doug Ladd, Stan Hudson and Alan Brant, who shared information on their recent discoveries of rare orchids in southeast Missouri.

Becky Haefner made the very fine drawings. Michael Homoya at the Indiana Department of Natural Resources, and Don Kurz and Rick Thom of the Missouri Department of Conservation generously provided excellent photographs. The orchid maps were produced by Diana Jarrell. I am indebted to Tom Toney for information on prairie orchids, and to Mervin Wallace and John Clinton who accompanied me on many field trips.

I am grateful to the curators of the various herbaria in Missouri for making their specimens available for research, and to the staff at the Field Museum of Natural History in Chicago for their generous assistance during my visit there.

Art and photo credits

Bill Summers – cover photo of showy lady-slipper orchid and photos on pages 16, 18, 42, 49, 52, 60, 62, 71, 73, 77, 79, 81, 88, 93, 95, 99, 101 and 102

Mike Homoya – photo on page 54

Don R. Kurz – photos on pages 20, 22, 24, 28, 34, 35, 38, 40, 47, 56, 64, 69, 75, 83, 86, 98 and 104

Richard H. Thom – photos on pages 23 and 90

Rebecca Haefner – pen and ink drawings

Drawings of *Platanthera leucophaea* (p. 41) and *Platanthera praeclara* (p. 43) reprinted with permission from *Rhodora,* Vol. 88(854): 269 (© 1986 by the New England Botanical Club).

Natural Divisions of Missouri
and their Sections

Glaciated Plains

- Western
- Grand River
- Eastern
- Lincoln Hills

Big Rivers

- Upper Missouri
- Lower Missouri
- Upper Mississippi
- Lower Mississippi

Ozark Border

- Missouri River
- Mississippi River

Ozark

- Springfield Plateau
- Upper Ozark
- St. Francois Mts.
- Elk River
- White River
- Lower Ozark

Mississippi Lowlands

- Crowley's Ridge
- Lowlands

Osage Plains

- Osage Plains

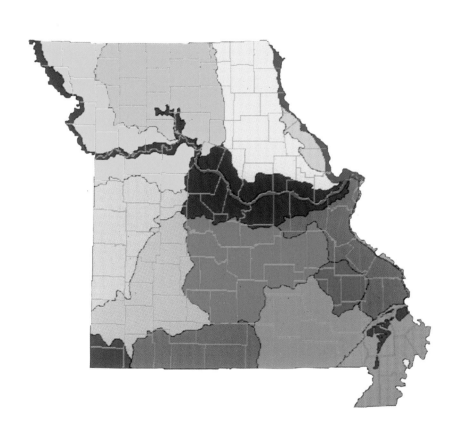

About This Book

This book is designed to enable the amateur botanist to identify Missouri orchids. Some technical terminology is used where needed, but all terms are defined in the glossary on pages 108–110. Measurements are given in inches and feet and in metric units. There is a short introduction to each genus followed by a key to the species when more than one species occurs in Missouri. I have tried to keep the keys simple, but unfortunately even simple keys are sometimes difficult to use. To aid in identification, each species is shown in its typical habitat. A drawing of the inflorescence is included for many of the smaller-flowered species. Each species description includes the common name or names, the period of flowering, a description of the habitat and statewide distribution, plus a brief description of the plants.

A list of frequently associated species is included when it might aid in the identification of suitable habitat. The statewide distribution is described by natural division (Thom and Wilson, 1981). For a map of the natural divisions, see page 9. In addition, a county distribution map is included for each species. Dots on each map indicate past and present verified populations. These are documented by the presence of voucher specimens in one or more herbaria (museums of pressed plants). An extensive search of specimens in Missouri and out-of-state herbaria was made during the course of this project. Sightings of orchid populations that have not been verified by specimens are included on the maps as triangles.

The main purpose of this book is to help people identify, appreciate and enjoy the beautiful and elusive orchids of Missouri. They are one of our precious natural resources and can provide much enjoyment to those who seek these plants in their native habitats.

How to Use the Keys

This key and those following are designed to help you identify orchids by their leaf and flower characteristics. The keys consist of a series of paired statements. Only one of the statements in each pair will be true for a given specimen. Choose the statement most closely describing the plant to be identified, then proceed to the next pair of statements indicated, and so on. For instance, let us assume that we have found an orchid with a single yellow flower. We begin with the first pair of statements: **A.** Flowers 1–4 to a stem, or **A.** Flowers 5 to many to a stem. Since our plant has only one flower, we choose the first statement in the pair, which directs us to statement pair **B.** Our orchid has a very large slipperlike flower, so we choose the first statement of pair **B,** which directs us to the genus *Cypripedium* on page 14. We can then compare our flower to the description on pages 14 and 15. If we wish, we can determine which species we have by using the key on page 15, or by comparing our flower to the photos on pages 16 and 18.

Caution: Do not pick an orchid. Bring your book with you and identify it in the field, or take close-up photos and make detailed notes of leaf and flower arrangement to which you can later refer.

Key to the Genera

A. Flowers 1–4 to a stem . . . . **B**
   B. Lip inflated, saclike, more than 2 cm long;
      anthers 2. . . . . *Cypripedium* p. 14
   B. Lip not inflated or saclike or, if so,
      then less than 1 cm long; anther 1 . . . . **C**
      C. Flowers with a prominent spur; leaves 2 at base of plant,
         broadly oval. . . . . *Galearis*, p. 24
      C. Flowers without a spur; leaves linear or, if oval,
         more than 2. . . . . **D**
         D. Flowers 1 or 2 per stem . . . . **E**
            E. Stem leaves in a whorl of 5 or 6; flower 1 (rarely 2),
               yellow-green. . . . . *Isotria*, p. 51
            E. Stem leaf 1, linear; flowers 1 or 2,
               pink . . . . *Pogonia*, p. 49

D. Flowers 3 or 4 (occasionally more in *Calopogon*) . . . . . . **F**

    F. Leaves cauline, alternate, 3 or 4, ovate; flowers whitish pink, appearing late July to early October, lip lowermost . . . . *Triphora*, p. 56

    F. Leaf nearly basal, 1, linear; flowers pink, appearing early May to early July, lip upper most . . . . *Calopogon*, p. 58

A. Flowers 5 to many to a stem . . . . **G**

  G. Leaves absent or barely persisting at flowering time . . . . **H**

    H. Green leaves produced, but usually not present at flowering; plants green . . . . **I**

      I. Leaves more than 1, absent during winter; inflorescence spiraled; flowers whitish . . . . *Spiranthes*, p. 67

      I. Leaf 1, green throughout winter, usually dried at flowering time; inflorescence not spiraled . . . . **J**

        J. Flowers with a spur, pale greenish purple or gray . . . . *Tipularia*, p. 101

        J. Flowers without a spur, yellowish purple . . . . *Aplectrum*, p. 98

    H. Green leaves never produced, plants brown or purple . . . . **K**

      K. Flowers 1 cm long at most, brown, yellow-green or white spotted with purple, lip only shallowly lobed or not at all . . . . *Corallorhiza*, p. 85

      K. Flowers 1.7–2.3 cm long, madder-purple, lip 3-lobed . . . . *Hexalectris*, p. 104

  G. Leaves present at flowering time . . . . **L**

    L. Leaves all basal or nearly so . . . . **M**

      M. Leaves 2, broadly oval . . . . *Liparis*, p. 92

      M. Leaves more than 2 or not oval . . . . **N**

        N. Leaves green throughout; lip not saclike; inflorescence spiraled . . . . *Spiranthes*, p. 67

        N. Leaves conspicuously marked with white; lip saclike; inflorescence not spiraled . . . . *Goodyera*, p. 83

    L. At least 1 or more cauline leaves present . . . . **O**

      O. Flowers spurred . . . . *Platanthera*, p. 26

      O. Flowers without spurs . . . . **P**

        P. Leaves several, cauline, alternate; flowers green with madder-purple . . . . *Epipactis*, p. 64

P. Leaf 1 (rarely 2); flowers pink or greenish . . . . **Q**

   Q. Leaf linear, grasslike, nearly basal; flowers pink,
      2–6 cm long . . . . *Calopogon*, p. 58

   Q. Leaf oval-elliptic, halfway up stem; flowers
      greenish, 2–3 mm long . . . . *Malaxis*, p. 90

CYPRIPEDIUM L.

Lady-slipper

Cypripedium is from the Greek *cypris,* a name for the goddess, Aphrodite, and *pedilon,* "shoe." The name aptly describes the lovely flowers that resemble the slippers of Aphrodite.

Common Names: Lady-slipper, moccasin-flower, golden-slipper, whip-poor-will shoe

Lady-slipper orchids are perennial plants ranging from 7 or 8 inches (18–20 cm) up to 3 feet (1 m) in height. They grow from coarse, fibrous root systems and are frequently colonial, with as many as 2 dozen plants growing in a clump. The plants are upright, and the stems of all species are hairy. Several broad, sharp-pointed leaves clasp the stem. These leaves are strongly ribbed or pleated lengthwise. In several species, the leaves are covered with glandular hairs, which, when touched, can cause a skin rash in some people. The stem ends with 1 or 2 (rarely 3) showy flowers, each growing from a green, leafy bract.

The distinguishing feature of members of this genus is the inflated lip, which gives the flowers the appearance of dainty slippers. The upper sepal and lateral petals are long and thin, half-twisting with wavy margins. The 2 lateral sepals are joined together beneath the lip.

The cavity of the lip is designed so that when a visiting insect attempts to leave the flower, it must squeeze by the stigma first and then the anther. In doing so, it deposits pollen from another flower on the stigma and picks up more pollen to be carried to the next flower.

There are 3 species of *Cypripedium* in Missouri. They are among our showiest native orchids. Lady-slipper orchids probably once were more common than they are today. Their woodland habitat has been disturbed by logging, grazing and conversion to pasture. The showy flowers have made these orchids favorites of collectors. Unfortunately, the plants rarely survive when transplanted. The roots of several species are reported to have medicinal value and are sought by root diggers.

In spite of all these pressures, the yellow lady-slipper, although not abundant, is not uncommon in Missouri. The small white lady-slipper and showy lady-slipper are rare, however, and should be protected.

Cypripedium kentuckiense C.F. Reed is another species of yellow lady-slipper known from the southern states. It is very similar to the *C. calceolus* group; however the lip is much larger, having a large opening, with the color varying from pale yellow to creamy yellow. Its range is from Louisiana to southeastern Oklahoma. A few of the northwestern Arkansas populations occur in counties adjacent to Missouri. In southwest Missouri, it should be sought along margins of small, spring-fed streams and fens in wooded situations.

I have learned that lady-slippers are much more easily found by starting at the bottom of a slope and looking upward. This is because the showy flowers tend to face downslope and are hidden from above by the leafy bract. To suddenly come upon a colony of lady-slipper orchids in full bloom is a sight to be remembered always. They will hold you spellbound until you suddenly realize that they are real and that nature, once again, is the perfect artist.

Key to the Species

A. Sepals and petals not twisted, shorter than or equal to the lip;
   lip rose or purplish with white . . . . **3.** *C. reginae*, p. 22
A. Sepals and lateral petals twisted, linear, acute,
   longer than the lip. . . . . **B**
   B. Lip white . . . . **2.** *C. candidum*, p. 20
   B. Lip yellow . . . . **C**
      C. Lip 3–5 cm long; lateral petals 5–9 cm long; sepals usually
         greenish yellow with purple lines; leaves 4 or 5 (rarely 6)
         on a stem . . . . **1a.** *C. calceolus* var. *pubescens*, p. 16
      C. Lip smaller, 2–3 cm long; lateral petals 3.5–8 cm long;
         sepals dull madder-purple; leaves usually 4–6 on
         a stem . . . . **1b.** *C. calceolus* var. *parviflorum*, p. 18

1. *Cypripedium calceolus* L.

Calceolus is from the Latin *calceus*, meaning "small shoe."

Common Name: Yellow lady-slipper orchid

There are 2 varieties of *C. calceolus* in Missouri.

1a. *C. calceolus* L. var. *pubescens* (Willd.) Correll

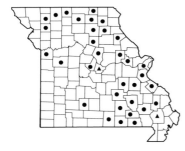

Pubescens refers to the hairiness of the plant.

Synonymy: *Cypripedium pubescens* Willd.

Common Name: Large yellow lady-slipper

Flowers late April through early June

Variety *pubescens* grows in acid soils on north- or east-facing slopes bordering streams, valleys or ravines in oak-hickory-pine woods. It has been reported from every natural division except the Mississippi Lowlands, but is most common in the Ozark Division.

This is the larger of the 2 varieties of yellow lady-slipper. The plants are from 8–28 inches (20–80 cm) tall, hairy, with 4–6 large oval, sharp-pointed leaves. The largest leaves may reach 8 inches (20 cm) long and 5 inches (12 cm) wide. The stem ends with 1 or 2 showy yellow flowers on arching stems.

The spreading sepals and petals are variable from shades of yellow-green to yellow-green that is lightly or heavily veined with brownish purple. The color on plants within a single colony may even vary from year to year. The upper sepal may be almost 3 inches (7.5 cm) long, arching over the lip. The 2 lateral sepals are united beneath the lip. The lateral petals are very long and thin and spiral loosely downward from the lip about 2–3 ½ inches (5–9 cm). The yellow, saclike lip resembles a shoe. It is inflated with a rounded opening on the top near the rear.

This variety is generally more robust than variety *parviflorum,* and the flowers are larger. Also, the sepals and petals are usually lighter in color. A rare albino form with a white lip has been recorded from Webster County.

Technical Description:
Perennials from coarse, fibrous roots; stems upright, solitary or more often colonial, 20–80 cm high; leaves 4–6, ovate-lanceolate, pointed, many-nerved, 10–20 cm long, 4–12 cm broad, pubescent; flowers 1 or 2, terminal; sepals and petals twisted, yellow-green, lightly to heavily veined with brownish purple, upper sepal arching over lip, lateral sepals united under lip; petals linear, twisted, 5–9 cm long, 5–10 mm broad; lip yellow, inflated, 3–5 cm long, 1.5–3.5 cm broad.

1b. *C. calceolus* L. var. *parviflorum* (Salisb.) Fern.

Parviflorum means "small-flowered."

Synonymy: *Cypripedium parviflorum* Salisb.

Common Name: Small yellow lady-slipper

Flowers late April through early June

The habitat for this variety is similar to that of var. *pubescens*. It is found most commonly throughout the western half of Missouri. Its range overlaps with that of var. *pubescens*.

The plants are upright with 3–6 broad, oval, sharp-pointed leaves clasping the stem. The leaves are hairy and strongly ribbed. Larger leaves may be up to 8 inches (20 cm) long and 5 inches (12 cm) wide. The stem ends with 1 or 2 (rarely 3) fragrant, nodding yellow flowers growing from a broad, leafy bract. The petals and sepals vary in color from yellowish brown to deep maroon. They are long and narrow with wavy margins, and are usually twisted. The upper sepal arches over the lip, and the lateral sepals are united beneath. Both petals and sepals are lightly to densely hairy near the base. The yellow lip is $^1/_2$–1 $^1/_2$ inches (1.2 – 4 cm) long and inflated, with an opening on the upper side near the back. Red stripes occur in the cavity and occasionally around the cavity opening. A rare albino form has been recorded from Shannon and Crawford counties. This variety is generally smaller in stature than the previous one and has small flowers.

Technical Description:
Perennials from coarse, fibrous roots; stems upright, solitary or colonial, 15 – 60 cm high; leaves 3 – 5, ovate-lanceolate, pointed, 5 – 20 cm long, 2.5 – 12 cm broad, many-nerved, pubescent; sepals and petals twisted, variable in color, yellow-brown to deep maroon, lateral sepals united under lip; petals linear, 3 – 9 cm long; lip yellow, inflated, 1 – 4 cm long, 1 – 2.5 cm broad, interior red-streaked; flowers fragrant.

2. *Cypripedium candidum* Muhl. Ex Willd.

Candidum is from the Latin *candidus,* meaning "white."

Common Name: Small white
                lady-slipper

Flowers late April through late May

The small white lady-slipper occurs in wet prairies, low wooded slopes bordering streams and seepy dolomite ledges in deep hollows. This species is very rare in Missouri, having been reported in the past from Atchison, Nodaway, Andrew, Shannon and St. Louis counties.

Until recently, the last documented sighting was by Steyermark in 1947 in Nodaway County. He found 15 plants on a west-facing slope bordering the One Hundred and Two River. In 1979, members of the Missouri Native Plant Society unsuccessfully searched the area for this species. More recently, a small population was discovered in a remote, rugged area of Howell County. Several colonies occur in this area, scattered along moist, seepy ledges of a dolomite bluff with dry sandstone outcrops above. At this site it is associated with *C. reginae*, the showy lady-slipper. Similar habitat occurs in several other deep hollows and side ravines in the rugged Ozarks of southern Missouri. It is hoped that additional populations may be discovered in the future.

This species is the smallest of the lady-slipper orchids, ranging from 6–16 inches (15–40 cm) tall. There are usually 3 or 4 lance-shaped leaves clasping the stem. The larger leaves may be up to 6 inches (15 cm) long and 2 inches (5 cm) wide and are strongly ribbed. The stem ends in 1 (very rarely 2) small, showy flower subtended by a leafy bract. The flower of this species looks like a small porcelain slipper. The inflated lip is white, delicately streaked with rose-purple and only $3/4-7/8$ inch (1.8–2.3 cm) long. The sepals and petals are greenish yellow with purplish stripes and are downy near the base. The upper sepal is about an inch (2.5 cm) long, slightly twisted and arches over the lip.

These diminutive lady-slippers have been prized by collectors for many years. Collecting pressure and loss of habitat have made this species very rare throughout the United States. Please report any sightings to the Missouri Department of Conservation.

Technical Description:
Perennials with fibrous roots; stems upright, solitary or colonial, 15–40 cm high; leaves 3 or 4, erect, lanceolate or narrow-elliptical, 5–15 cm long, 1–5 cm broad, many nerved, finely pubescent; flowers 1 (rarely 2), fragrant; sepals and petals greenish yellow, purple streaked; upper sepal lanceolate, 2–3 cm long, arching over lip, lateral sepals united under lip; petals linear-lanceolate, twisted, 2.5–3.5 cm long; lip white, purple-striped within, 1.8–2.3 cm long; staminode yellow; seed capsule elliptical, 2–2.5 cm long.

3. *Cypripedium reginae* Walt.

Reginae means "of the queen" and refers to the beautiful, stately flower of this species.

Synonymy: *Cypripedium spectabile* Salisb.

Common Name: Showy lady-slipper

Flowers mid-May through early June

The showy lady-slipper grows in moist crevices of north-facing limestone bluffs, along small streams and in fens (calcareous wet meadows). It is reported from Carter, Douglas, Howell, Iron, Oregon, Ozark, Shannon and Texas counties in the Ozark Division. It also was reported from Putnam County, where it was collected by Bush, but Steyermark (1963) was unable to locate Bush's sites.

This orchid has one of the most beautiful, showy flowers in Missouri. It also is one of the largest lady-slippers, growing up to 3 feet (1 m) or more in height. There may be up to 10 broad, oval leaves on a single stem, and the larger leaves may be as much as 10 inches (25 cm) long and 6 inches (15 cm) wide. The stems and leaves are covered with hairs that cause dermatitis in some people.

The stem ends in 1 or 2 (rarely 3) showy flowers, each subtended by a leafy bract. The inflated lip is white, suffused with broad bands of rose-purple or pink, and 1–2 inches (3–5 cm) long. The sepals and petals also are white, oval and somewhat blunt, and are shorter than the lip. They are not twisted like those of other *Cypripedium* species.

This orchid, like the small white lady-slipper, has been prized by collectors. It is rare in Missouri, but several rather large populations still exist. Fortunately, the species occurs in remote areas where it is less accessible to would-be collectors. Like other *Cypripedium* species, it is often colonial, and a colony in full bloom is an incredible sight.

Technical Description:
Perennials from fibrous roots; stems upright, solitary or colonial, 0.3–1 m high; leaves 5–10, erect, ovate-lanceolate, up to 25 cm long, 15 cm broad, pubescent, strongly nerved; flowers terminal, 1 or 2 (rarely 3); sepals and petals white, blunt, shorter than lip; upper sepal elliptical-ovoid, arching over lip, 3–4.5 cm long, lower sepals united; petals ovate lanceolate, flat, spreading; lip inflated, white with pink or rose-purple, 3–5 cm long; sterile stamen white with pink and yellow; capsule erect, 2.5–4.5 cm long.

GALEARIS Raf.

Orchis

Galearis spectabilis (L.) Raf.

Galearis is from the Greek *galea,* "hood" in reference to the convergence of sepals and petals formed above the lower lip.

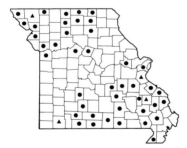

Synonymy: *Orchis spectabilis* L. (Luer, 1975)

Common Name: Showy orchis

Flowers late April to early June

This species occurs below bluffs; in rich, shaded woods; on humus-covered slopes; in low, wooded valleys along streams; in ravine bottoms; and in rich, sandy, acidic or calcareous soils.

Showy orchis is a woodland species, found in oak-hickory and oak-hickory-pine forests. The plant occurs infrequently throughout the state, but is generally absent from the Osage Plains and Mississippi Lowlands divisions.

Plants average about 8 inches (20 cm) tall when flowering; the flowering stalk arises from a cluster of fleshy, thickened roots. There are 2 (rarely 3) leaves clasping a slender, 4- or 5-angled stem at ground level. The dark green leaves are broad and blunt at the ends, about 2 1/2 inches (6 cm) wide and 8 inches (20 cm) long.

Each plant has from 3–12 flowers in a loose raceme, and each flower is supported by a leafy bract. The flowers are purple or lavender with a white lip. The lip is spade-shaped with a blunt spur curving downward.

In one location in Ozark County, the species occurs in rich woods at the base of a small limestone bluff. Among the associated species also found at this site are Christmas fern, tall bellflower, spotted jewelweed, white avens, elm-leaf goldenrod, aster, beggar ticks, white snakeroot, ebony spleenwort, red and white oak, white ash, sycamore and hickory.

At one time, showy orchis was reportedly found in large numbers in certain wooded valleys throughout the state. In recent years, fewer plants are seen.

Technical Description:
Plants 5–15 cm high from fleshy-tuberous roots; leaves basal, 2 (rarely 3) oblong-obovate, dark green, 7–20 cm long; scape 4–5 angled, 3–12 flowers in a raceme, each with a foliaceous bract; perianth pink, lilac, purplish or white, 1.5–3 cm long, galeate above lip; lip white, ovate, reduced at base with blunt spur extending downward.

PLATANTHERA L.C. Rich.

Platanthera comes from the Greek *platys,* "wider" or "broad," and *anthera,* "anther," in reference to the unusually wide anther in this group.

The genus name *Habenaria* was used for this group in the first edition of *Missouri Orchids,* to be consistent with the *Flora of Missouri* (Steyermark, 1963) and other older references. *Platanthera* is now the name accepted by most botanists for this group of orchids, and it is used in most recent publications, including Yatskievych and Turner (1990).

Members of the genus *Platanthera* are perennial plants growing from fleshy, tuberous roots. They range in height from only a few inches to more than 3 feet (1 m). All have 1 or more fairly large, lance-shaped leaves clasping the lower third of the stem. The stem ends in a showy flower spike or raceme. The flowers usually are fragrant, and in several species they are brightly colored. All species are characterized by a long spur extending down from the lip base.

There are 8 *Platanthera* species in Missouri.

Key to the Species

A. Lip (largest petal) smooth or minutely toothed or appearing
as if gnawed, but not fringed or deeply divided . . . . **B**
    B. Lip 2- or 3-toothed or with 2–3 short lobes;
    1 well-developed leaf on stem (rarely 2); bracts shorter
    than the flowers . . . . **1.** *P. clavellata,* p. 28
    B. Lip smooth or minutely toothed or gnawed;
    leaves 2–5 on stem; bracts equal to or longer
    than the flowers. . . . . **2.** *P. flava,* p. 31

A. Lip (largest petal) deeply divided or fringed, or both . . . . **C**
    C. Lip fringed but not lobed or divided, flowers
    bright yellow to orange . . . . **3.** *P. ciliaris,* p. 35
    C. Lip deeply 3-lobed. . . . . **D**
        D. Flowers white or greenish white; lip deeply fringed,
        the fringe as long or longer than the body of the lobe;
        1–4 larger lower leaves, 0.5–5 cm broad . . . . **E**

E. Flowers white, yellow-white, tinged with bronze; spur 1–1.7 cm long; petals linear to spatula shaped, blunt, not toothed. . . . . **4.** *P. lacera*, p. 38

E. Flowers creamy white to greenish white, showy; spur 2–5.5 cm long; petals toothed, oval or triangular; rare. . . . . **F**

    F. Spur 2–4 cm long, slender, 1.3 mm in diameter; columns small and rounded, viscidia facing each other 1.2–3.2 mm apart; petals white, sepals greenish; raceme loose. . . . . **5.** *P. leucophaea*, p. 40

    F. Spur 3.6–5.5 cm long, thicker, 2.7 mm in diameter; columns larger and angular, viscidia directed somewhat forward 6.2–7.5 mm apart; petal and sepals creamy white; raceme dense. . . . . **6.** *P. praeclara*, p. 42

D. Flowers lilac, rose-pink or magenta; lobes of lip shallowly fringed or merely toothed; largest leaves 2–9 cm broad . . **G**

G. Lobes fringed, fringe 2–5 mm long. . **7.** *P. psycodes*, p. 45

G. Lobes shallowly toothed or appearing as if gnawed . . . . **8.** *P. peramoena*, p. 47

1. *Platanthera clavellata* (Michx.) Luer.

Clavellata is from the Latin *clava*, "club," referring to the club-shaped spur of this species.

Synonymy: *Orchis clavellata* Michx.
Orchis tridentata Muhl. ex Willd.
Habenaria tridentata (Muhl.) Hook.
Gymnadeniopsis clavellata (Michx.) Rydb.
Habenaria clavellata (Michx.) Spreng.

Common Names: Green wood orchid, wood orchid, green woodland orchis, frogspike

Flowers July to August

The green wood orchid occurs along the margins of spring branches and seeps, and in swampy woodlands. It is known from Butler, Carter, Dunklin, Stoddard and Wayne counties in the Southeastern Lowlands,

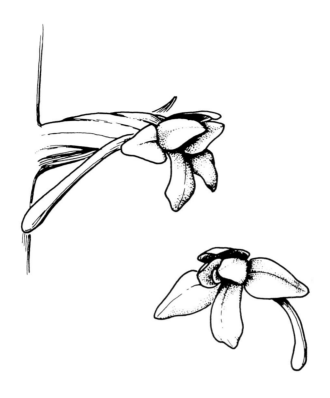

RAH

and locally in St. Francois and Bollinger counties.

This slender species grows from 4–18 inches (10–45 cm) tall from slender, slightly fleshy roots. One well-developed leaf (rarely 2) clasps the stem near the base. The leaf is narrowly oblong with a blunt end, tapering to a narrow stalk where it clasps the stem. It may be up to 9 inches (23 cm) long and 1 inch (2.5 cm) wide. Upper stem leaves are greatly reduced, becoming bractlike near the top. The stem ends in a spike of small clustered flowers. Botany manuals list the flowers as being white, green, yellow or greenish yellow; however, the Missouri plants I observed had white or very pale yellow flowers, but not green. The flowers are usually turned at odd angles to each other, with the lip sideways or upside down. The flowers are less than $1/2$ inch (1 cm) long. The upper sepal and lateral petals form a hood over the lip, and the 2 lateral sepals spread away from the lip. The oblong lip is unlobed and has 3 rounded teeth at the end. A long, slender spur with a swollen tip curves from the lip base.

The green wood orchid was first discovered in Missouri on July 21, 1900, near Kennett in Dunklin County. Rebecca Haefner discovered a new site on Sept. 9, 1979, in Bollinger County. At this site she found about 200 fruiting plants along the margin of a sinkhole pond. This species occurs at several locations in Stoddard County, along with another rare plant, *Bartonia paniculata* var. *paniculata. Bartonia* is a member of the gentian family and is known only from the base of Crowley's Ridge. Here both species occur with American holly, *Ilex opaca,* which also is rare in Missouri. In recent years several new sites have been discovered in southeastern Missouri.

Technical Description:
Glabrous, slender plants, 7–45 cm high; roots slender, slightly fleshy; lower leaf (rarely 2) narrowly oblanceolate, spatulate or narrowly oblong, blunt, tapering to petiolar base, 5–23 cm long, 0.7–2.7 cm thick; flowers divergent, greenish, greenish yellow or white, 2–5 mm long; petals and sepals similar, oblong-ovate, upper sepal and petals forming hood, lateral sepals spreading; lip cuneate-oblong with 3 rounded teeth; spur slender, clavate at apex, exceeding ovary; bracts lanceolate to ovate, acuminate, shorter than ovary.

2. *Platanthera flava* (L.) Lindl.

The species name is from the Latin *flavidus*, "yellow," and refers to the flower color. However, the flowers are more typically green or greenish white.

Synonymy: *Orchis flava* L.
   Perularia flava (L.) Farw.
   Habenaria flava (L.) R. Br.

Common Names: Pale green orchid, southern rein orchid, northern rein orchid

Flowers mid-May to September

Plants of this species grow in low, wet woods and bottomlands bordering streams and in swales of wet prairies. Two varieties of *P. flava* occur in Missouri.

A. Inflorescence loosely flowered, floral bracts equaling the flowers; larger stem leaves usually 2 (occasionally 3) . . . . **2a.** *P. flava* var. *flava*, p. 32

A. Inflorescence compact, lowest floral bracts much longer than flowers; larger stem leaves, 2–5 . . . . **2b.** *P. flava* var. *herbiola*, p. 34

2a. *Platanthera flava* var. *flava*

Synonymy: *Habenaria flava* (L.) R. Br. var. *flava*

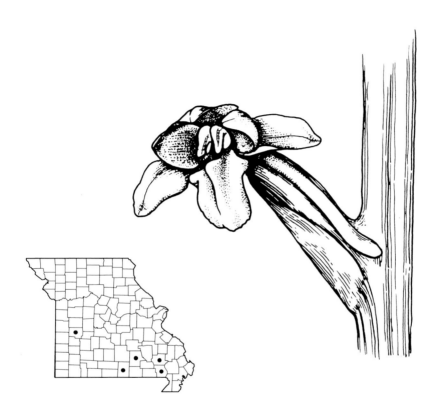

This variety is found only in Butler, Howell, Shannon and Wayne counties in the southern Ozarks and in St. Clair County in western Missouri.

The plants are slender, 4–24 inches (10–60 cm) high and grow from fleshy, thickened tubers. There are generally 2 (although occasionally 1 or 3) well-developed leaves on the lower portion of the stem. The larger of these may be up to 7 inches (18 cm) long and 2 inches (5 cm) wide, tapering to a point. The upper leaves are reduced in size. The stem ends with a loose spike of flowers from 1–7 inches (2.5–18 cm) long. The greenish yellow flowers are reported to be sweet-smelling. They are sessile in the axils of the floral bracts, which are equal in length to the flowers. The sepals are oblong, up to $\frac{1}{2}$ inch (1 cm) long

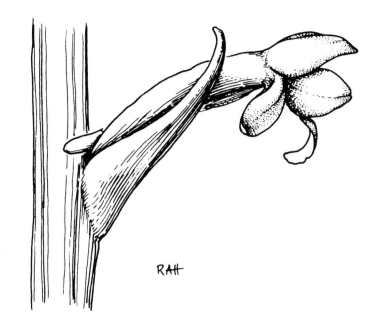

and occasionally have small teeth.

The petals are similar but broader. The lip is about ¹/₂ inch (1 cm) long, oval to rounded in shape and slightly toothed at the end. A slender spur extends from the base of the lip, usually farther than the ovary.

Approximately 100 plants of this variety were recently found in St. Clair County on a native prairie. The plants occupied a narrow belt about a quarter of a mile long between very dry, sandy soil and seasonally wet soils.

2b. *P. flava* var. *herbiola* (R. Br.) Luer

Synonymy: *Orchis virescens* Muhl. ex Willd.
Habenaria herbiola R. Br.
Habenaria virescens (Muhl.) Spreng.
Habenaria flava (L.) R. Br. var. *virescens* (Muhl.) Fernald
Habenaria flava var. *herbiola* (R. Br.) Ames & Correll

This variety has been collected more frequently in the past than var. *flava*. The plants appear stouter than do those of var. *flava*. There are usually more than 2 larger lower leaves, and these are broader. The spike of flowers is compact, and the conspicuous lower floral bracts are longer than the flowers.

Technical Description:
Glabrous, slender plants, 10–70 cm high; roots fleshy, thickened tubers; lower leaves 1–5, well-developed, lanceolate-oblong or elliptical, tapering to apex, 6–20 cm long, 1–5 cm broad; flowers in loose or

compact spike, greenish or greenish yellow; sepals and petals similar, oblong to ovate or suborbicular, 2–5 mm long, petals dentate at summit; lip ovate to suborbicular, crenate; floral bracts equal to or exceeding perianth.

3. *Platanthera ciliaris* (L.) Lindl.

Ciliaris is from the Latin *cilium*, "hair," and refers to the hairlike fringe on the lip.

Synonymy: *Orchis ciliaris* L.
　　　　　Blephariglottis ciliaris (L.) Rydb.
　　　　　Habenaria ciliaris (L.) R. Br.

Common Names: Yellow fringed orchid, orange plume

Flowers late July to early October

The yellow fringed orchid occurs in woods and thickets bordering spring branches and in the margins of sinkhole ponds. In the past it has been collected from Iron, Ripley and Stoddard counties in southeastern Missouri, and more recently from Carter, St. Francois and Wayne counties. There are four extant sites in the state.

Yellow fringed orchids are smooth, rich-green plants growing up to 3 feet (1 m) tall. Large, well-developed leaves up to 10 inches (25 cm) long are present on the lower part of the stem; upper stem leaves are reduced in size. The stem ends in a short raceme of very showy yellow-orange flowers. The sepals are rounded, whereas the petals are narrow. The upper sepal and lateral petals join to form a hood over the lip. The lip is oval and deeply fringed. The slender spur is curved and from $^5/_8$–1 $^1/_4$ inches (1.2–3 cm) long.

The delicately fringed, bright-colored flowers make this one of the most beautiful of the Missouri orchids.

This is another of the rare species that inhabits Crowley's Ridge near its junction with the lowlands. Here the orchid grows in association with American holly *(Ilex opaca).*

Technical Description:
Glabrous perennials 30 – 90 cm high; roots fleshy-thickened tuberoids; lower cauline leaves lanceolate, acuminate, up to 25 cm long, upper leaves reduced; flowers in a short spike, orange to yellow-orange; ovary linear, stalklike; style 7–12 mm long; sepals orbicular, 6 – 8 mm long; petals lanceolate or oblong, apex dentate; lip oblong to ovate with ciliate margins; spur 1.5 –2.5 cm, equaling or exceeding ovary; bracts linear-lanceolate, attenuate, equaling or exceeding ovary.

4. *Platanthera lacera* (Michx.) G. Don var. *lacera*

The specific name is derived from the Latin *lacerare*, "to cut," and refers to the lip, which appears cut or torn.

Synonymy: *Orchis lacera* Michx.
Blephariglottis lacera (Michx.) Rydb.
Habenaria lacera (Michx.) Lodd. var. *lacera*

Common Names: Ragged orchid, ragged orchis, green fringed orchid

Flowers mid-May to early August

This species occurs in upland meadows and prairies, moist woods, and along the margins of sinkhole ponds. It is found most frequently in the native prairies of the Osage Plains Division, but also occurs in scattered counties of the Ozark and Ozark Border divisions.

Plants of this species range from 8–30 inches (20–75 cm) in height.

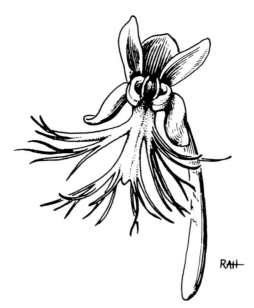

There are 3–9 well developed leaves on the lower stem. These are narrowly oblong and are from 2 1/2–8 inches (6–20 cm) long and 3/8–1 3/8 inches (1–3.5 cm) broad. The upper stem leaves are reduced to bracts. The stem ends with a spike of deeply fringed flowers, which are pale yellow to greenish white and often bronze-tinged. The flowers are quite fragrant. The sepals are rounded, and the upper one joins with the narrow lateral petals to form a hood over the lip. The lip is deeply 3-lobed, and each lobe is long-fringed. The curved spur is about 3/8–5/8 inch (1–1.7 cm) long.

This is the most common *Platanthera* species in Missouri. It looks very similar to the much rarer *P. leucophaea,* but the spur of *P. leucophaea* is much longer than that of *P. lacera,* about 3/4–1 1/2 inches (2–4 cm), and the flowers generally are whiter.

Technical Description:
Plants slender, glabrous, 20–80 cm high; roots thickened tuberoids; lower leaves 4–9, well developed, narrowly oblong to lanceolate, 6–20 cm long, 1–3.5 cm broad, upper leaves bracteose; spike slender, loosely flowered, 5–30 cm long, 2–6 cm thick; flowers green, yellow green, pale yellow or white, often bronze-tinged, fragrant; perianth 4–6 mm long; sepals oblong to suborbicular; petals linear-lanceolate; lip tripartite, fringed, 1–1.5 cm long; floral bracts linear-lanceolate, acuminate.

5. *Platanthera leucophaea* (Nutt.) Lindl.

Leucophaea refers to the white flowers of this species.

Synonymy: *Orchis leucophaea* Nutt.
Blephariglottis leucophaea (Nutt.) Rydb.
Habenaria leucophaea (Nutt.) Gray

Common Name: Eastern prairie fringed orchid

Flowers mid-June to early July

The eastern prairie fringed orchid grows primarily in wet prairies and fens (calcareous wet meadows). It has been recorded in counties of the Glaciated Plains, Ozark and Ozark Border divisions, although it has not been found in Missouri for several years.

Plants of this species are generally larger than *P. lacera*, reaching up to 4 feet (1.3 m) tall. There are up to 6 well-developed lower leaves,

which are up to 8 inches (20 cm) long, and $^5/_8$–1 $^3/_8$ inches (1.5–3.5 cm) wide. The leaves are keeled and pale green in color. The upper leaves are reduced to bracts. The stem ends in a loose, showy raceme, up to 8 inches (20 cm) long, of deeply fringed flowers. The petals are white with green sepals, and the flowers emit a pleasing fragrance at dusk, which attracts sphinx moths as pollinators.

The rounded upper sepal and spatulate lateral petals form a hood over the anther column. The column is small and rounded, and the viscidia are directly below the pollinia and facing each other, only $^1/_{20}$ – $^1/_8$ inch (1.2–3.2 mm) apart. The spur is $^3/_4$–2 inches (2–4 cm) long and slender, $^1/_{14}$ inch (1.8 mm) in diameter. The 3-lobed lip is up to $^3/_4$ inch long (1.5–2 cm) and deeply fringed.

Technical Description:
Glabrous perennial plants 0.2–1.3 m high; lower leaves 3–6, up to 20 cm long, 1.5–5 cm broad, keeled, elliptic to lanceolate, clasping, upper

leaves reduced; flowers in a loose raceme 3–20 cm long; flowers fragrant, white to greenish white; sepals ovate; petals obovate, apex dentate, 8–10 mm long, erect, connivent with upper sepal; lateral sepals spreading; lip 1.5–2 cm long, tripartite, lacerated; spur 2–4 cm long, 1.8 mm in diameter, clavellate; column narrow, lobes rounded, narrow, the viscidia 1.2–3.2 mm apart.

6. *Platanthera praeclara* Sheviak & Bowles

Praeclara, which means very bright, beautiful or splendid, refers to the very showy flowers of this species.

Common Name: Western prairie fringed orchid

Flowers mid-June to early July

This species was described by Sheviak and Bowles in 1986 to account for differences they observed in *P. leucophaea* specimens from the western portion of its range. They observed these specimens to differ in flower size, spur length and diameter, and column structure, among other differences.

The major difference between the 2 species is their column structure. The column (united style and stamens) in *P. leucophaea* is small and rounded. The viscidia (the sticky mass attached to the pollen that adheres to pollinators) are facing each other and are only $^1/_{20}$–$^1/_8$ inch (1.2–3.2 mm) apart. The column of *P. praeclara* is much larger and noticeably angular. The viscidia are directed somewhat forward and are wider, $^1/_4$–$^1/_3$ inch (6.2–7.5 mm) apart.

The difference in column structure serves to reproductively isolate the 2 species. Both flower at the same time, and both are pollinated by sphinx moths. However, the pollinaria of *P. leucophaea* are deposited on the moth's proboscis, whereas *P. praeclara* pollinaria attach to the eyes. Differences in stigma orientation in each species prevent pollen of one from being transferred to the other.

The plants of *P. praeclara* tend to be shorter than *P. leucophaea,* ranging from 10–33 inches (25–85 cm) high. The raceme is often shorter (5–11 cm) with fewer flowers, but the flowers are larger and more densely arranged, making this a very showy species. The flowers are creamy white, and the spurs are very long (3.6–5.5 cm) and thick, 2.7 mm in diameter. The flowers emit a light, sweet fragrance that intensifies at dusk.

The range of *P. praeclara,* as described by Sheviak and Bowles, extends into eastern Kansas, Nebraska, eastern North and South Dakota, Minnesota, Iowa and western Missouri, where it occurs in dry-mesic and mesic upland prairies. It is known historically from Clinton, Greene, Jackson, Jasper, Johnson, Lawrence, Newton and Vernon counties.

Three populations of this species are extant in Atchison, Harrison and Holt counties in northwest Missouri. In Atchison County, the plants occur in the swales of a dry-mesic upland prairie. The plants I observed there ranged from 10–24 inches (25–61 cm) tall and were well camouflaged by taller grasses and forbs. Ten years passed between sightings of the species there, in spite of annual searches by botanists.

Technical Description:
Glabrous, pale green, perennial plants, 25–85 cm high, erect, stout; lower leaves 3–6, up to 26 cm long, 5 cm wide, keeled, lanceolate to ovate-lanceolate, ascending, clasping; upper leaves reduced; raceme large, showy, 4.8–11.6 cm long, 5.5–9 cm broad; flowers creamy white, large, fragrant; sepals ovate to suborbicular, 9–14.1 mm long, 6.8–10 mm wide; petals flabelliform, apex lacerate; lip 1.7–3.2 cm long, 2–3.9 cm broad, tripartite, lacerate; spur 3.6–5.5 cm long, 2.7 mm in diameter, clavellate; column broad, lobes triangular, wide spreading, the viscidia 6–7 mm apart.

7. *Platanthera psycodes* (L.) Lindl.

The specific name is from the Greek *psyche,* "butterfly," in reference to the shape of the flower. It is sometimes incorrectly spelled *psychodes.*

RAH

Synonymy: *Orchis psycodes* L.
Blephariglottis psycodes (L.) Rydb.
Habenaria psycodes (L.) Spreng.

Common Names: Small purple fringed orchid, soldier's plume

Flowers July through August

This species is included in Missouri's flora on the basis of a single plant seen by Julian Steyermark in the wildflower garden of William Bauer of Webster Groves in St. Louis County (Steyermark, 1963). Bauer had found the plant along Caney Creek in the Caney Mountain Refuge of

Ozark County. On a visit to the site in 1949, Steyermark and Bauer were unable to locate any plants; a tree had fallen where Bauer remembered seeing them. The species has not been found in Missouri since then.

In states where it occurs, the purple fringed orchid grows in moist woodlands along streams and in moist meadows. The plants range in height from 8 inches to 3 feet (20–90 cm). Two to 5 well-developed leaves clasp the lower stem. The stem ends in a dense, showy raceme of purple flowers. The raceme may be as much as 9 inches (23 cm) long and 3 inches (7 cm) thick. The fragrant flowers are about ½ inch (1 cm) long. The lip is 3-lobed, and each lobe is deeply fringed.

Technical Description:
Perennial plants, 20–90 cm high, from tuberous roots; lower leaves well-developed, 2–5, oblanceolate-elliptic, 2–7 cm broad, upper leaves reduced; raceme dense, 5–25 cm long, 2.5–4.5 cm thick; flowers lilac-pink to deep rose-purple, fragrant; sepals oval; petals flabellate or spatulate, dentate or entire at summit, 4–7 mm long; lip 6–16 mm long, 3-lobed, each lobe deeply lacerated spur equaling ovary in length.

8. *Platanthera peramoena* (A. Gray) A. Gray

Peramoena is a Latin adjective meaning "very lovely."

Synonymy: *Blephariglottis peramoena* (A. Gray) Rydb.
Habenaria peramoena A. Gray

Common Names: Purple fringeless orchid, pride-of-the peak

Flowers late June to early September

This species occurs in rocky, moist woods along small streams, wooded lake margins and low wet woods in the St. Francois Mountains Section of the Ozark Division and in the Ozark Border and Mississippi Lowlands divisions.

The purple fringeless orchid is a rather large, impressive plant up to 3 feet (90 cm) tall. As many as 5 well-developed leaves are present on the lower third of the stem. The longest of these may reach 7 inches (18 cm) and be up to 2 inches (5 cm) wide. The stem ends in a dense

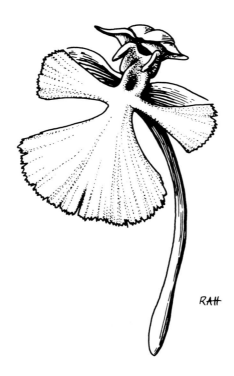

spike of striking deep-pink to purple flowers. The spike may be up to 7 inches (18 cm) long and almost 3 inches (7 cm) thick. The fan-shaped petals and the upper sepal form a hood over the anther column. The lateral sepals are elliptical. Both sepals and petals are about $^1/_4$–$^3/_8$ inch (6–10 mm) long. The lip divides into 3 spreading lobes and is about $^1/_2$–$^3/_4$ inch (13–22 mm) long. The end of each lobe is toothed, as if an insect has gnawed the edges. The spur is long and slender. A rare albino form was discovered by Carol Dodds in Butler County.

Technical Description:
Upright, glabrous plants to 90 cm high; lower leaves 3–5, well-developed, to 17.5 cm long, 5 cm broad, upper leaves reduced; spike showy, 17 cm long, 5 cm thick, deep pink or purple; sepals elliptic, upper connivent with lateral petals, lateral ones spreading, lateral petals truncate; lip spreading, 3-lobed, lateral lobes truncate, apex erose, terminal lobe truncate, apex rounded, erose; spur slender, equaling ovary; anther column winged, pollen masses 2.

POGONIA Juss.

Snake-mouth

Pogonia ophioglossoides (L.) Ker. Gawl.

Pogonia, "bearded," refers to the lip. *Ophis,* "serpent," and *glossa,* "tongue," also refer to the ragged, tonguelike lip of the species.

Common Names: Snake-mouth, pogonia

Flowers June to early July

This species was first discovered in the state by William Bauer in 1948. It is known from only two locations. It is restricted to fens (calcareous wet meadows) in Reynolds and Shannon counties that are open and predominately covered with grasses and sedges. The orchids are distributed throughout the fens, occurring on small tussocks.

The plants are slender and average 5–15 inches (13–40 cm) in height with a single erect leaf midway up the stem. The leaf is lance-shaped to oblong or elliptical and is about 1–4 1/2 inches (2.5–11.5 cm) long and 1/2–1 1/4 inches (0.5–3 cm) wide.

There are 1 or 2 terminal flowers, each supported by a leafy bract. The first flower matures before the second one opens. The second flower, when present, is usually smaller, not as well formed and is a duller pink. The flowers are about 1/2–1 inch (1–2.5 cm) long and are fragrant and showy. Colors range from very pale to rich, deep pink. The sepals and petals are similar in appearance. The lateral sepals are spreading. The lip is spatula-shaped with its margins deeply cut. The upper surface is densely crested or bearded. The front portion of the crest is pink, changing abruptly to yellow/yellow-green, with brown at the tip. The flowers fall away very soon after pollination.

Associated species include Indian paintbrush, royal fern, grass-of-Parnassus, phlox, yellow loosestrife, flax, marsh blue violet, rush (*Scirpus polyphyllus*), and brown-eyed Susan (*Rudbeckia fulgida*). At one of the sites, it grows with *Utricularia subulata*, a tiny, terrestrial bladderwort that was first documented to occur in Missouri during a 1995 field trip of the Webster Groves Nature Study Society.

Technical Description:
Plants glabrous, 12–40 cm high; roots horizontal, up to 8 cm long; basal petioled leaves lanceolate to oblong or narrowly obovate; flowering stem slender, erect; cauline leaf narrowly lanceolate to narrowly obovate or elliptical, 1–15 cm long; the blunt oblong to narrowly elliptical sepals and the broader petals spreading; beard or crest of entire lip of 3 rows of elongated yellow or brown-tipped processes; flowers fragrant.

ISOTRIA Raf.

Whorled pogonia

The name is from the Greek *isos*, "equal," and *treis*, "three," in reference to the 3 equal sepals that are characteristic of the genus.

Synonymy: *Pogonia* Nutt.

The genus *Isotria* is made up of perennial plants growing from long, slender roots. The slender stems end in a whorl of 5 or more leaves. One (rarely 2) flowers grow on short pedicels (stalks) directly above the leaves.

Isotria generally forms colonies of sterile (non-flowering) and flowering plants. The sterile plants usually occur more frequently. Members of the genus *Isotria* are quite rare. They occur in acid soil of dry woods, usually on slopes or terraces adjacent to small streams.

Two species of *Isotria* have been recorded in Missouri; both are rare.

A. Sepals linear, 3–6 cm long, more than twice
   as long as the petals; flower stalk (peduncle) as long as
   the ovary or longer .... **1.** *I. verticillata*, p. 52
A. Sepals linear-lanceolate, 1.5–2.5 cm long, as long as
   the petals or only 1 ½ times longer; flower stalk shorter
   than the ovary .... **2.** *I. medeoloides*, p. 54

1. *Isotria verticillata* (Muhl. ex Willd.) Raf.

Verticillata refers to the whorled leaves.

Synonymy: *Pogonia verticillata* Nutt.

Common Name: Large whorled pogonia

Flowers late April to May

This species occurs in acid soil on wooded slopes and level terraces adjacent to streams. In Missouri, it is known from Butler, Oregon, St. Francois, Ste. Genevieve and Stoddard counties.

The plants average from 6–10 inches (15–25 cm) in height, although taller plants have been recorded. They grow from long cord-like roots that frequently send up new plants, forming colonies of flowering and non-flowering plants. These colonies are similar to those of May apples but not as dense. A naked stem ends with a whorl of 5 (occasionally 6 or 10) leaves, above which occurs a single flower (rarely 2) on a short stalk.

The small plants emerge with the whorl of leaves folded upright, embracing the erect flower bud. As the flower opens, the plant becomes erect and the whorl of leaves spreads.

The leaves are oblong, about 4 inches (10 cm) long and 1 1/4 inches (3 cm) wide. The distinctive flower has 3 very narrow, greenish brown sepals, 2 or more inches (5 cm) long. The sepals are broadest at the base and gradually taper toward the tip with enrolled margins. The 1-inch long (2.5 cm), yellow-green, lateral petals overlap, forming a hood over the lip. The lip is trough-shaped and 3-lobed. The terminal lobe is white with reflexed, undulating margins, and the side lobes are deep purple-brown with white along the margins. A yellow crest occurs along the median. The flower parts drop away immediately after pollination, and the ovary develops into an upright seed capsule.

This rare and local orchid was first found in Missouri in 1897 in Butler County (Steyermark, 1963). This site no longer exists. However, a site was discovered in Ste. Genevieve County in 1952 by five members of the St. Louis-based Webster Groves Nature Study Society, and was reported by Oscar Petersen of that group. This orchid has since been recorded from several localities in southeastern Missouri.

The roots apparently do not send up plants every year. Many plants apparently do not flower, but remain vegetative some years.

Technical Description:
Roots horizontal, long, cordlike, creeping underground, often sending up new plants; stem naked, terminated by a whorl of 5, 6 or more leaves embracing a single (rarely 2) erect flower; leaves at first upright, soon spreading, obovate, elliptic to subcuneate, 4–10 cm long, 0.7–1.5 cm broad; peduncle 2.5–3.5 cm long; sepals 3.5–6 cm long, yellow-green at base, madder-purple above, linear, broad at base, tapering with inrolled margins, somewhat spreading; petals yellow-green, 1.5–2.5 cm long; lip narrowly oblong, obovate, 3-lobed, terminal lobe white with reflexed undulating margins, lateral lobes deep madder-purple with white margins, crest yellow-green; capsule 2.5–3.5 cm long, peduncle 2.5–6 cm long.

2. *Isotria medeoloides* (Pursh) Raf.

Named for *Medeola virginiana* (lily family) because of the striking vegetative similarity between the two species

Synonymy: *Arethusa medeoloides* Pursh
Pogonia affinis Aust.
Isotria affinis Rydb.
Odonectis affinis Schlecter

Common Name: Small whorled pogonia

Flowers in May

An 1897 collection by Colton Russell of *Isotria medeoloides* from a wooded limestone hill in Bollinger County is the only known record of this plant in Missouri.

The plants of this species may reach 10 inches (25 cm) in height.

They grow from short, cordlike roots that, on rare occasions, sprout and send up new plants, forming small colonies of flowering and non-flowering plants. The naked stem ends with a whorl of 5 or more reflexed leaves above which are 1 or 2 flowers on short stalks. The leaves are narrowly elliptical up to 2 1/2 inches (6 cm) long. The flowers are greenish yellow and about 1 inch (2.5 cm) long. The arching sepals are 1/2–1 inch (1–2.5 cm) long, and the petals are 1/4–1/2 inch (5–10 mm) long. The pale green lip is 3-lobed.

This orchid is very rare throughout its range.

Technical Description:
Roots short, horizontal, cordlike, rarely producing sprouts; scapes terminated by whorls of 5, 6 or more leaves, becoming reflexed; leaves 3.5–6 cm long, narrow rhombic-elliptic; flowers 1–2, greenish yellow; peduncles 1.3–2.5 cm; sepals arching, 1.5–2.5 cm long; petals 1.2–1.5 cm long; lip yellow-green, 3-lobed, narrowly obovate, lobes subequal; seed capsule 1.3–2.5 cm long, peduncle 0.5–2 cm.

Triphora trianthophora (Sw.) Rydb.

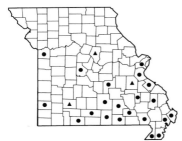

Both the generic and specific names are from Greek *treis,* "three," and *pharus,* "bearing," in reference to the flowers, which frequently grow in threes.

Synonymy: *Pogonia pendula* Lindl.
  Pogonia trianthophora (Sw.) BSP.
  Triphora trianthophora var. *schaffneri* Camp

Common Names: Nodding pogonia, three-bird orchid

Flowers late July to early October

This species occurs in rich woods along slopes, in low valleys, along creeks, and in alluvial lowland forests. It is widely scattered in southern Missouri, north to Jackson County and east to St. Louis County.

This fragile orchid has lavender and green stems, and averages 3 – 4 inches (7.5 – 10 cm) in height, although it may grow as tall as 12 inches (35 cm). The plants grow from small, round tubers that send out horizontal stolons tipped with small tubers. These smaller tubers give rise to new plants, forming small colonies. There are 3 or 4 alternate, oval leaves. Two or 3 (occasionally 4) flowers occur singly in the upper leaf axils. The flowers are very small, $^1/_2 - ^3/_4$ inch (1–1.5 cm) long, and white, pink or pinkish white on slender stalks. The flowers are nodding while in bud, becoming upright when open. The sepals are lance-shaped and longer than the petals, spreading away from the petals and lip. The 3 lobed lip is narrowed near the base and dilated near the center with flared, undulating margins at the end. The lip has 3 green longitudinal lines. Dried flowers do not fall from the plant, but remain on the seed capsules.

This orchid, like many others, may exist for years underground without sending up flowering plants.

Technical Description:
Fragile plants of woodlands, 3–30 cm high, arising from elongated tubers; tubers sending out horizontal stolons tipped by small tubers that produce new plants; leaves ovate, small; flowers usually 3, axillary; perianth 1–1.5 cm long, white, pink or pinkish white on slender peduncles, nodding in bud, ascending or nodding in anthesis; sepals lanceolate, terminal one arching, lateral ones spreading, exceeding petals and lip in length; petals close; lip 3-lobed, terminal lobe longest, narrowed at base, dilated with flared undulating margins at apex, with 3 green longitudinal lines; anther column subcylindric, with 2 red purple flanges, pollen grains purple; seed capsules cylindric, 1–1.5 cm long, 0.5 –1 cm thick, ascending or reflexed.

CALOPOGON R. Br.

Grass Pink

From the Greek *calas*, "beautiful," and *pogon*, "bearded," in reference to the hairs on the lip.

Synonymy: *Limodorum* L.

The genus *Calopogon* is made up of perennial plants growing from a solid bulblike tuber. At the base of the flowering stem is a single elongate leaf. The erect flowering stem has 2–10 flowers in a spike-like raceme at the tip.

Plants in this genus generally occur as scattered individuals in the habitats where they grow. Members of *Calopogon* are uncommon. They occur in saturated soils of open calcareous fens, wet soils on slopes or terraces adjacent to small streams, drier parts of low prairies, and dry ridgetops and slopes in upland prairies. Plants at a given site apparently fluctuate in numbers from year to year.

Calopogon is one of the few North American orchids in which the lip is the uppermost portion of the flower. Most orchid flowers twist while opening so that the lip is on the bottom.

Until recently, grass pinks in the state were treated as a single species by most authors. I first discussed (Summers, 1987) the fact that in Missouri these orchids exhibit two morphological phases that coincide with two different habitats. Subsequently, Magrath and Nelson (1989) examined similar variations in Oklahoma plants and treated them as *C. tuberosus* var. *tuberosus* and var. *simpsonii*, (Chapman) L. Magrath, respectively. In Arkansas, Slaughter (1993) treated the plants as *C. tuberosus* var. *tuberosus*. More recently, Goldman (1995) concluded that these phases represent distinct species, and his classification is followed in this text.

Two species of Calopogon have been recorded in Missouri, both are uncommon.

A. Flowering stem and leaf about same length; petals and sepals pale to deep pink, clump of club-shaped hairs nearest the tip of the lip pale pink (lower clumps usually yellow) . . . . **1.** *C. oklahomensis,* p. 60

A. Flowering stem much longer than leaf; petals and sepals magenta to rose-pink; clump of club-shaped hair nearest the tip of the lip white with gold tips (lower clumps usually magenta to rose-pink) . . . . **2.** *C. tuberosus,* p. 62

1. *Calopogon oklahomensis* D.H. Goldman

Oklahomensis is named for the state where the type specimen was collected.

Synonymy: *Calopogon pulchellus* (Salisb.) R. Br. in part
  Calopogon tuberosus (L.) BSP. in part

Common Name: Prairie grass pink

Flowers early May to early June

This species occurs in upland prairies in the Osage Plains of southwestern Missouri and locally in the Ozark Division in Howell County. Prairie grass pink ranges in height from 4–14 inches (10–36 cm) with a single grasslike leaf sheathing the stem at the base. There are one or two short sheaths just above the tuber. The leaf is usually about the same height as the inflorescence, sometimes a little shorter or longer.

The slender stem ends in a rather compact raceme of 2–8 flowers. The lower buds open first. The flowers range from 1–2 inches (2.5–5 cm) across and vary from pale to deep pink.

The sepals are sharply pointed, the 2 lateral ones sickle-shaped, and the lower one lance shaped. The 2 lateral petals also are sickle-shaped, though not as sharply-pointed as the sepals. The sepals and petals spread outward, exposing the anther column. The lateral sepals tend to reflex backwards with age. The lip, or upper petal, is fan-shaped on top, gradually narrowing toward the bottom with 2 rounded basal lobes. The upper portion of the lip is covered with club-shaped hairs. The anther column is slender and winged at the end, with 2 pollen masses on the wings.

In Howell County, this orchid occurs in the drier portion of a low prairie. Plants have been observed to flower in quick succession compared to *C. tuberosus*. On May 9, one plant was observed with the lowest two flowers fully open. On May 12, it had five flowers fully open at one time. On May 14, only the two uppermost flowers were fully open. The next day, all were withered.

Technical Description:
Plant 10-36 cm high; scape arising from a single forked corm up to 2.5 cm long; leaf usually single elongate, linear-lanceolate, 0.5–1.5 broad, 5–36 cm long, usually 1 or 2 sheaths below. Flowers in a terminal, spiciform raceme, rather compact with 2–8 non-resupinate flowers, these opening in rather quick succession; pale to deep pink, 2–5 cm broad, sessile in the axils of small acute bracts along a slightly geniculate rachis; lateral sepals spreading, ovate lanceolate, falcate; lower sepal lanceolate, reflexed upward at apex; lateral petals spreading, ovate-lanceolate, somewhat falcate, with undulate upper margins; labellum uppermost, linear-oblong, flabellate at summit, 5–15 mm broad; bearded near summit with clavellate tipped hair. Anther column parallel with lower sepal, similar in color to petals and sepals, winged at summit.

2. *Calopogon tuberosus* (L.) BSP.

The specific name refers to the tuberous root.

Synonymy: *Calopogon pulchellus* (Salisb.) R. Br.
Limodorum tuberosum L.
Limodorum pulchellum Salisb.

Common Name: Grass pink, swamp pink

Flowers June to early July

This species occurs in fens (calcareous wet meadows) and occasionally in moist open woods, and is scattered in counties of the Lower Ozark and St. Francois Mountain sections of the Ozark Natural Division in the southeastern portion of the state.

Grass pink grows to 27 inches (69 cm) tall with a single grasslike leaf sheathing the stem at the base. There are usually one or two short sheaths just above the corm. The leaf is usually much shorter than the inflorescence. The slender stem ends in a loose spikelike raceme of 3–10 showy flowers. The flowers range from 1–2 ½ inches (2.5–6.2 cm) across and may be rose, pink or magenta, with deeper-colored veining in the sepals and petals. The sepals and petals spread outward, exposing the anther column, which is the same color. The sepals are sharply pointed, the 2 lateral ones are sickle-shaped and the lower one lance-shaped. The 2 lateral petals also are sickle-shaped, though not as sharply pointed as the sepals. The upper margins are slightly wavy. The lip, or upper petal, is linear at the base, with 2 rounded lobes; toward the top it becomes broadly triangular or fan-shaped at the tip. The upper portion of the lip is covered with club-shaped hairs. They are magenta, rose-pink and white. The white ones are gold-tipped and resemble pollen-laden anthers that attract bees and other insects to the flower. The actual anther column is slender and winged at the end, with 2 pollen masses on each wing.

This species of *Calopogon* is more showy than *C. oklahomensis*. It tends to have larger, more brightly colored flowers that stay open longer, and the plant is usually taller. This species appears to be restricted to calcareous fens in the southeastern Ozark Division of the state. It ranges from St. Francois County southwest to Shannon and Carter counties.

More study needs to be done on the 2 species of *Calopogon* in Missouri to better determine their characters and habitat ranges.

Technical Description:

Plant 10–69 cm high. Scape arising from a solid bulblike corm; leaf usually single elongate, linear-lanceolate, oblong 0.2–4 cm broad, 5–50 cm long. Flowers 2.5–6.2 cm broad, magenta or rose-pink; 3–10 non-resupinate flowers in a loosely spiciform raceme, sessile in axils of small acute bracts along a slightly geniculate rachis. Lateral sepals spreading (sometimes reflexing backwards with age), ovate-lanceolate, falcate; lower sepal lanceolate, reflexed upward at apex; lateral petals spreading, ovate-lanceolate, somewhat falcate, with undulate upper margins, labellum uppermost, linear-oblong, flabellate at summit, 5–15 mm broad, the base with 2 rounded lobes; bearded at summit with magenta, rose-pink, and white clavellate tipped hair, the white ones yellow-gold tipped; the anther column similar in color to petals and sepals, parallel with lower sepal, winged at summit; capsules erect, 1–2 cm long, 5–10 mm broad, perianth persisting.

EPIPACTIS Zinn.

Helleborine

Epipactis is the ancient name for hellebore.

Synonymy: *Serapias* L. in part.
Helleborine Mill.
Amesia Nels. & Macbr.

Epipactis helleborine (L.) Crantz

The specific name refers to the similar appearance of these plants to those of the European genus *Helleborus* (buttercup family).

Synonymy: *Epipactis latifolia* (L.) All.

Common Name: Helleborine

Flowers late June to September

Epipactis helleborine is native to Europe and was introduced in North America. It is the only introduced orchid in Missouri.

RAH

Helleborine grows up to 3 feet (1 m) tall and looks somewhat like false Solomon's seal, *Maianthemum racemosum*. The species is characterized by alternate leaves that clasp the stem. The leaves are strongly veined and may be up to 7 inches (18 cm) long and 3 inches (7.5 cm) wide. They are oval-lance shape with a sharp point. The flowers are in a loose to somewhat dense raceme, each in the axil of a long, narrow floral bract. The flowers are greenish, suffused with dull purple or rose. The sepals and petals are lance-shaped to oval, with the lateral sepals being slightly longer than the petals, about ¹/₂ inch (1 cm) long. The lip is similar in color to the sepals and petals. It is triangular, with the terminal portion folded back, forming a sac.

This species was first introduced into eastern Canada and the northeastern United States in New York and New Jersey, and has found its way westward into Missouri. Sheviak (1974) reports this species invading disturbed woodlands, often along paths where trampling occurs, and that it is rapidly increasing in the Chicago area.

This species was known in Missouri only from Jasper County near Joplin, where it was found by Palmer in 1928. However, in 1983 it was reported from St. Louis County in a shaded backyard. It most likely came in by accident when the new homeowner transplanted some different flowers from New York.

Technical Description:
Plants 3–90 cm high, leafy; leaves clasping, ovate to lanceolate, acute, conspicuously nerved; raceme 5–25 cm, loosely to densely flowered, often 1-sided; flowers bracteose, 1 cm long, green suffused with madder-purple; sepals ovate-lanceolate, keeled; petals shorter, ovate, acute; lip saclike at base.

SPIRANTHES L.C. Rich.

Ladies' tresses, pearl twist

The generic name *Spiranthes* is from the Greek *speria*, "spiral," and *anthos*, "flower," in reference to the spiraled inflorescence characteristic of the genus.

Synonymy: *Gyrostachys* Pers.
              Ibidium Salisb.

Common Names: Ladies' tresses orchid, pearl twist

This is the most complex genus of orchids in Missouri. It is made up of plants with short, thickened roots and upright stems. The stem leaves are reduced to bracts or sheaths, and in some species may not be noticeable without a 10x hand lens. All species have linear basal leaves, which may or may not be present at flowering time.

The genus is characterized by an inflorescence of small, white to yellowish flowers arranged in 1 or more spiral rows. The flowers are sessile (without a stalk), and each is supported by a sharply pointed floral bract. The 2 upper petals and 1 upper sepal form a hood over the lip (lower petal). The hood and lip join, giving the flower a tubular appearance. The lateral sepals close on either side of the tube. The flowers of this genus are very small, some being only $^1/_8$ inch (3 mm) long. Close examination with a hand lens reveals the true orchid shape in miniature. An average inflorescence flowers for about 2 weeks, with the flowers at the bottom opening first.

There are 7 species of *Spiranthes* in Missouri, and they are difficult to tell apart. Habitat, flowering season, floral structure, odor and color, leaf shape, and presence must all be considered in identification. A 10x hand lens is a must for close-up study.

A. Perianth (sepals and petals) 6–11 mm long, plants
15–100 cm tall . . . . **B**
  B. Plants tall, 50–100 cm; basal leaves present at flowering;
    flowers in a loose, single spiral, appearing June to
    early September . . . . **3.** *S. vernalis*, p. 73
  B. Plants shorter, 10–57 cm; basal leaves usually absent at
    flowering, flowers in a dense spiral of 2 or more ranks,
    appearing August to November . . . . **C**
    C. Flowers very fragrant, 7–11 mm, cream colored, center
      of the lip usually yellowish; lateral sepals spreading;
      leaves absent at flowering; plants primarily of limestone
      and dolomite glades . . . . **5.** *S. magnicamporum*, p. 77
    C. Flowers with no fragrance or only faintly scented,
      6–11 mm, white, center of lip white; lateral sepals
      parallel petals; leaves occasionally present
      at flowering, usually wilted; plants of more
      acidic soils. . . . . **4.** *S. cernua*, p. 75

A. Perianth (sepals and petals) 3.5–7 mm, plants 5–55 cm tall . . . **D**
  D. Leaves present at flowering; flowers arranged in dense spiral
    of 2 or more ranks . . . . **E**
    E. Perianth 4–5 mm; lip white; flowers mid-September
      to October; rare . . . . **6.** *S. ovalis*, p. 79
    E. Perianth 5–7 mm; lip white with orange-yellow center;
      flowers late May-June . . . . **7.** *S. lucida*, p. 81
  D. Leaves absent at flowering; flowers usually arranged
    in a single, loose spiral . . . . **F**
    F. Perianth 3–4.5 mm long; lip white; root a solitary tuber;
      basal leaves absent at flowering . . . . **1.** *S. tuberosa*, p. 69
    F. Perianth 4–6 mm long; lip white with green center;
      roots 2 or more; basal leaves occasionally present
      at flowering, usually wilting. . . . . **2.** *S. lacera*, p. 71

1. *Spiranthes tuberosa* Raf.

Tuberosa is of Latin origin and refers to the swollen root.

Synonymy: *Spiranthes beckii* Lindl.
　　　　　　Spiranthes grayi Ames
　　　　　　Spiranthes tuberosa var. *grayi* (Ames) Fernald
　　　　　　Ibidium beckii (Lindl.) House

Common Name: Little ladies' tresses

Flowers mid-August through October

Little ladies' tresses occurs in acid soils of dry upland oak-hickory or pine-oak forests, on ridges, slopes and blufftops, and on dry upland prairies and meadows. The species has been found in every natural division, but is more common in the eastern half of the state.

This is one of the most delicate ladies' tresses in Missouri. The plants are very slender, dark green and smooth, without hairs. Plants range from 6–18 inches (15–50 cm) tall and emerge from a single thickened root. The basal leaves are oval, appearing in early spring and lasting until mid-summer, but are not present when the plant flowers, beginning in late July or early August. The flowers occur in a single rank or spiral and are spaced slightly apart. They are white and very small, about ⅛–¼ inch (3–4.5 mm) long. The flared lip has a crisp, waxy appearance. The lateral sepals turn inward along the floral tube.

This ladies' tresses is common in the state and can be found quite easily during the flowering season in its preferred habitat.

Technical Description:
Plants dark green, glabrous, from solitary (rarely 2–3) thickened root, 15–50 cm high, 1 mm thick; leaves 2–3, basal, ovate 1–2 cm long, 0.5–1 cm wide, absent at anthesis; spike 1–9 cm long, single-ranked, spiral or rarely secund, rachis glabrous; flowers white, 3–4.5 mm long, tubular; lip flaring, erose or crispy; bracts ovate, shorter than ovary.

RAH

2. *Spiranthes lacera* (Raf.) Raf.

Lacera is from the Latin *lacerare,* "torn," and refers to the irregularly cleft lip.

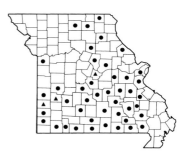

Synonymy: *Neottia lacera* Raf.
                  Spiranthes gracilis (Bigel.) Beck

Common Name: Slender ladies' tresses

Flowers mid-August through October

This species occurs in habitat similar to that of *S. tuberosa* in acid soils of dry, upland pine-oak or oak-hickory woods and on ridgetops and bluffs. It is most frequently found in the Ozark Division, but also is known from the Osage Plains and Ozark Border divisions and the Grand River Section of the Glaciated Plains Division.

    As its common name implies, this is a very slender, delicate plant. The stem has a diameter of less than ¹/₁₆ inch (1 mm) just below the inflorescence, a trait which it shares with *S. tuberosa. Spiranthes lacera* is usually taller than *S. tuberosa,* up to 20 inches (55 cm), which accentuates its slender nature. The dark green plants grow from 2 or 3 fleshy, thickened roots. The 2 or 3 basal leaves are oval and develop in the autumn or early spring. They usually wither by the time of flowering, but on rare occasions remain fresh.

The stem ends with a gently twisting spike of evenly spaced flowers, making this one of the more beautiful *Spiranthes.* The flowers are $^1/_8-^1/_4$ inch (4–6 mm) long and are white with green on the center of the lip. The sepals and petals form a tube over the irregularly cleft lip, spreading outward and downwards at the tips.

Because the habitats of *S. tuberosa* and *S. lacera* are similar, they occasionally may be found growing together. *Spiranthes lacera* is usually taller, appears more slender and generally has a more regular, graceful spiral of flowers.

The flowers of *S. lacera* have the green-centered lip. Also, *S. lacera* grows from 2 or 3 fleshy roots whereas *S. tuberosa* generally has only 1. If you dig the plants to aid in identification, please do so carefully and immediately replace them. The roots should be used in identification only as a last resort, and then only if there are many individual plants at the site.

Two very similar forms of this species that are sometimes recognized as varieties have been recorded in the state. The common, widespread var. *lacera* has the spike more loosely twisted, and the flowers are spaced further apart, generally not overlapping. The less common var. *gracilis* (Bigel.) Luer has been recorded from several counties. It has the spike more tightly twisted and the flowers spaced more closely together, usually overlapping.

Technical Description:
Plants 15–55 cm high; roots 2–3, fleshy-thickened; leaves basal, ovate-oblong, 1–4 cm long, 0.5–1 cm broad, thin, usually wilted at anthesis; spike slender, 1.5–11 cm long, 1-ranked, glabrous or nearly so; flowers white, 4–6 mm long; lip trough-shaped with irregular, flaring edges, center green.

3. *Spiranthes vernalis* Engelm. & A. Gray

Vernalis is of Latin origin and means "of spring." In Missouri, plants bloom in late summer.

Synonymy: *Ibidium vernale* (Engelm. & A. Gray) House

Common Names: Ladies' tresses, vernal ladies' tresses

Flowers June to early September

This ladies' tresses occurs in primarily acid soils of swampy meadows and upland prairies. It is infrequent and scattered south of the Missouri River. Most records for this species are old ones. It has not been observed much in recent years.

This is the tallest *Spiranthes* in Missouri, often reaching 2 feet (70 cm) or more. Long, linear leaves are present at the base of the stem at flowering. The stem ends in a spike up to 7 inches (18 cm) long, with the flowers arranged somewhat densely in a single rank. The entire inflorescence is covered with downy hairs. The flowers are white with a pale yellow lip. The lateral sepals form a tube and open down and outward from the lip at the ends. The floral bracts are oval and sharp pointed and are longer than the ovary.

Technical Description:

Plants 0.5–1 m high, light green; basal leaves erect, linear, 5–26 cm long, 0.2–1.5 cm broad, present at flowering; roots 2 or more, fleshy; spike 6–18 cm long, secund or spiraling, downy pubescent; perianth white or yellowish, 6–11 mm long; lip pale yellow, troughlike with flaring, crisp margins.

RAH

4. *Spiranthes cernua* (L.) L.C. Rich.

Cernua means "nodding" or "drooping," and refers to the flowers of this species.

Synonymy: *Ophrys cernua* L.
Gyrostachys ochroleuca Rydb.
Ibidium cernuum (L.) House

Common Names: Common ladies' tresses, nodding ladies' tresses, screw-auger

Flowers early August through November

Spiranthes cernua occurs on acid soil glades, dry upland prairies, and in wet meadows and thickets. It is scattered throughout Missouri, but is most common south of the Missouri River. This is the most common *Spiranthes* in Missouri.

This species is made up of a very complex group of plants and consists of several poorly defined varieties that will not be discussed in this book.

The plants grow anywhere from 6–18 inches (10–50 cm) tall from 1 to several fleshy roots. Three or 4 basal leaves emerge in early spring. The leaves vary in length from 1–9 inches (2.5–23 cm) and are up to 1 inch (2.5 cm) broad. They are usually withered by flowering. The lower stem leaves are linear and up to 2 inches (5 cm) long. The upper stem leaves are reduced. The stem ends in a spike of white flowers arranged in 2 or more spiral ranks of irregularly spaced flowers. The spike ranges from 1–6 inches (2.5–15 cm) long and $^{1}/_{2}$–1 $^{1}/_{4}$ inches (1.5–3 cm) thick. The stem of the spike is somewhat hairy. The flowers are fairly large, about $^{1}/_{4}$–$^{3}/_{8}$ inch (7–11 mm) long and nodding. The floral bract is oval with a long, narrow point and is half as long as the flower.

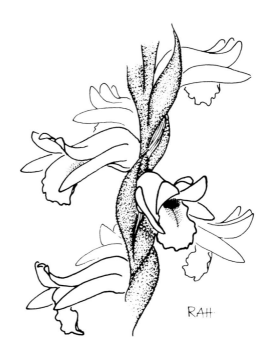

This species is very similar to *Spiranthes magnicamporum*. A description of the differences between the two is included in the account for *S. magnicamporum*.

Technical Description:
Plants 10–50 cm high; roots 1 to several, fleshy; leaves basal, linear-lanceolate to oblong, 2–23 cm long, 0.4–2 cm broad, rarely persisting until anthesis; cauline leaves linear, lower ones up to 5 cm long, upper ones reduced; spike 2–15 cm long, 1.5–3 cm thick, dense, pubescent, 2 or more ranked; flowers 5–10 mm, exceeding bracts, white, tubular, unscented; sepals and petals lanceolate, lateral sepals and petals lanceolate, lateral sepals appressed; lip oblong with flaring, crisp margins; seed with 2 embryos.

5. *Spiranthes magnicamporum* Sheviak

The Latin word *magnicamporum* means "of the Great Plains," indicating the habitat of this species.

Synonymy: *Spiranthes cernua* (L.) L.C. Rich., in part
                 Spiranthes cernua var. *odorata* (Nutt.) Correll

Common Name: Great Plains ladies' tresses

Flowers mid-September through November

This species was described by Sheviak in 1973 from specimens collected in Illinois. There has not yet been an extensive search for it in Missouri. It is very closely related to *Spiranthes cernua;* and in Illinois, it occurs in calcareous soils of loess bluff hill prairies, with a different race occurring on low black-soil prairies (Sheviak, 1973). In Missouri, we would expect to find the Great Plains ladies' tresses on limestone glades and calcareous soils throughout the Ozarks. This orchid may be fairly common in Missouri because many reports of *S. cernua* may, in fact, be *S. magnicamprum*. These species occupy somewhat different habitats in Illinois. *Spiranthes cernua* is more an acid soil species, occurring in sandy areas and generally requiring more moisture. *Spiranthes magnicamporum* requires calcareous soils and is more tolerant of dry conditions.

The Great Plains ladies' tresses is fairly large, ranging from 6–22 inches (15–57 cm) tall. It grows from several thickened, tuberous roots, which are usually larger than those of *S. cernua.*

The basal leaves are linear and are up to 5 1/4 inches (14 cm) long and 1/2 inch (12 mm) wide. They emerge in early spring and disappear before flowering occurs. They are never present during flowering, whereas the leaves of *S. cernua* occasionally remain until the plants flower.

The stem ends with a dense spike about 1 1/2–7 inches (4–18 cm) long and 5/8–1 1/8 inches (15–28 mm) thick. The flowers are arranged in 2 or more spiraling ranks. The flowers of this species are generally larger than those of *S. cernua,* often exceeding 3/8 inch (1 cm) in length. The lateral sepals are spreading, unlike those of *S. cernua,* which closely parallel the petals.

The flowers are cream-colored, and the center of the lip is usually yellow. They are strongly scented with the odor of coumarin. The flowers of *S. cernua* are only faintly scented or not scented at all.

Technical Description:
Plants erect, 15–57 cm tall; roots fleshy; leaves basal, linear-lanceolate, up to 14 cm long, 12 mm broad, absent at flowering; spike dense, 1.5–2.8 cm thick, 4–18 cm long; flowers in 2 or more ranks, fragrant, cream-colored, lip with yellow center; perianth 7–12 mm long; lateral sepals spreading.

6. *Spiranthes ovalis* Lindl. var. *erostellata* Catling

The Latin species name refers to the oval-shaped lip, and *erostellata* refers to the lack of a rostellum (part of the column in most orchid flowers) in plants of this variety.

Synonymy: *Ibidium ovale* (Lindl.) House

Common Name: Ladies' tresses

Flowers mid-September to early October

Spiranthes ovalis grows in low, rich woods and terraced slopes along streams and in rich, shady old fields taken over by young forest in either creek bottoms or flat ridgetops. This uncommon species is found in a number of counties throughout Missouri, but its occurrence is limited to one or only a few plants at any given site.

Plants of this species range from 6–16 inches (15–40 cm) high, are slender and grow from several thickened roots. The dark green leaves are linear in shape with their broadest portion nearest the end, tapering toward the base. They may grow up to 10 inches (25.5 cm) long and 1/4 inch (2 cm) wide and are without hairs. The leaves are present when the plants flower. The stem ends in a crowded spike covered with downy hairs. The white tubular flowers are arranged in a beautiful 2- or 3-ranked spiral. The flowers are only 1/8–3/16 inch (4–5 mm) long. The lateral sepals are held close to the floral tube, and the lip is oval in shape. In my opinion, this species is the most graceful of all the *Spiranthes*.

RAH

Technical Description:

Plants dark green, glabrous, 15–50 cm tall; roots several, thickened; leaves basal and cauline, dark green, oblanceolate, larger ones 4-23 cm long, 0.5–2 cm broad, present at anthesis; spike 1.5–8 cm long, 1–2.5 cm thick, 2- or 3-ranked; perianth 4–5 mm long, white, tubular, nodding; lateral sepals appressed; lip ovate.

7. *Spiranthes lucida* (H. H. Eaton) Ames

Lucida is from the Latin *lucere,* "to shine," and refers to the shiny basal leaves.

Synonymy: *Neottia plantaginea* Raf.
  Spiranthes plantaginea (Raf.) Lindl.
  Neottia lucida H.H. Eaton
  Spiranthes latifolia Torr. ex Lindl.
  Ibidium plantagineum (Raf.) House

Common Name: Yellow-lipped ladies' tresses

Flowers late May to mid-June

This species occurs in fens (calcareous wet meadows) and along the bases and moist ledges of sandstone or limestone bluffs bordering creeks. It occurs only in the Ozark Division.

This is the only spring-flowering *Spiranthes* in Missouri. The plants range from 3–15 inches (7.5–38 cm) in height. The basal leaves are broad, ¹/₂–1 inch (1.5–2.5 cm), compared to other *Spiranthes* and are present when the plant flowers. The stem ends with a dense spike of flowers arranged in 2–4 spiraling ranks. The spike is usually smooth, but may be slightly hairy. The flowers are white, tubular and small, ¹/₈–¹/₄ inch (4–7 mm) long. The lip is squarish and has a bright orange-yellow center.

The species is uncommon in Missouri. Its early flowering period and yellow lip make it one of the easier *Spiranthes* to identify.

Technical Description:
Plants 5–38 cm high; roots several, thickened; leaves basal and cauline, oblong oblanceolate, dark green, basal ones 3–11 cm long, 0.5–2 cm broad, present at anthesis; spike 1–8 cm long, glabrous or puberulent; perianth white, 4–7 mm long; lip squarish oblong, center bright orange-yellow; upper sepals and petals rounded at apex; lateral sepals appressed.

RAH

82

GOODYERA R. Br.

Rattlesnake Plantain

The genus is named for John Goodyer, an English botanist of the 17th century.

Goodyera pubescens (Willd.) R. Br.

The specific name *pubescens* refers to the downy appearance of the plant.

Synonymy: *Neottia pubescens* Willd.
Peramium pubescens (Willd.) MacMillan
Epipactis pubescens (Willd.) A.A. Eaton

Common Names: Rattlesnake plantain, lattice leaf

Flowers late July to mid-September

The rattlesnake plantain favors acid soils overlaying sandstone or chert in deep, cool ravines and narrow canyons, and the lower portions of steep north-facing slopes. It is rare and scattered in the Ozark and Ozark Border divisions.

Plants of this species grow 6–18 inches (15–50 cm) tall from fleshy, creeping rhizomes that may produce small colonies of plants. The entire plant is covered with downy hairs. Each plant has a basal rosette of 5–10 leaves. The distinctive leaves of this species make it easy to identify in the winter. They are dark green, laced with a network of white veins. One slender stem rises from the rosette of leaves with small, linear bracts alternating along its length. The stem ends with a dense spike of small, whitish flowers. On rare occasions plants are found with all the flowers to one side of the spike. The sessile, globe-shaped flowers are ¹/₈–¹/₄ inch (4–6 mm) long and grouped closely together. The upper sepals and petals join to form a hood over the lip. The lateral sepals are broad and enclose the saclike lip on the sides.

Occasionally, colonies of rattlesnake plantain grow quite large. A colony in Douglas County was 3 feet long and 18 inches wide in places. The plant generally occurs where leaf accumulation is thin and mosses and lichens cover the ground. It also has been observed growing in small cracks on the faces of sandstone bluffs.

Some plants frequently found associated with rattlesnake plantain include partridge berry, wild azalea, green adder's mouth orchid, small yellow lady-slipper orchid, lily twayblade, spikenard, round-lobed hepatica, Christmas fern, maiden-hair fern, fragile fern and ebony spleenwort. Steyermark (1963) reported this species from only Douglas, Iron, Reynolds and Ste. Genevieve counties. Since the publication of his *Flora of Missouri* in 1963, it has been found in Howell, Shannon and Texas counties.

Technical Description:
Plants 15–50 cm high, pubescent, from fleshy creeping rhizomes; leaves a basal rosette of 5–10, ovate to ovate-lanceolate, 3–8 cm long, 1.5–3 cm broad, evergreen, dark green with white veins; scape 3–5 mm thick; raceme dense, oblong-cylindric or rarely secund, 2–11 cm long, 1.5–2 mm thick; perianth 4–6 mm long, sessile; lip saccate with beak; capsules globose, sessile, 4–10 mm long, 3–6 mm broad.

CORALLORHIZA Gagnebin

Coral root

From the Greek *corallion,* "coral," and *rhiza,* "root," in reference to the resemblance of the rhizome to pieces of coral.

The coral roots are woodland species found throughout southern Missouri and infrequently in the northern counties. They occur in dry or moist woods, on ridges and slopes, in ravine bottoms and along streams in rocky or non-rocky soils.

Coral roots are leafless plants ranging in height from 2–15 inches (5–38 cm). Their stems are purplish, reddish or yellow-green. Three or 4 inconspicuous, sheathlike leaves occur alternately on the stem. The stem ends with a raceme of 2–25 very small flowers. The flowers are purple-white or purple-brown, depending on the species.

Members of this genus are saprophytic and get all of their nutrients from the mycorrhizal fungi associated with their roots. Because they lack chlorophyll, they cannot photosynthesize and thus are unable to capture and utilize the sun's energy.

Plants grow singly or in colonies. They sometimes grow and flower profusely at a site and then disappear for several years.

Earlier reports of *C. trifida* Chatel. var. *verna* (Nutt.) Fernald from Lawrence and Warren counties (Steyermark, 1963; Summers, 1987) were based upon misdetermined specimens of the albino form of *C. wisteriana.* This albino form has now been recorded in Franklin, Lawrence and Warren counties.

There are 2 species of coral roots in Missouri. Both are common.

Key to the Species

A. Blooming in the late summer and fall; flowers 3–4 mm long,
   lip entire.............................. **1.** *C. odontorhiza,* p. 86

A. Blooming in the spring; flowers 4.5–8 mm long;
   lip notched .... **2.** *C. wisteriana,* p. 88

1. *Corallorhiza odontorhiza* (Willd.) Nutt.

Odontorhiza refers to the "toothed" roots.

Common Names: Late coral root, autumn coral root

Flowers August to November

The late coral root occurs in rich or rocky soil on ridgetops, glade margins, ravines, wooded slopes and low, wooded valleys in dry or moist conditions. This coral root is scattered throughout the state, but is less common than *C. wisteriana*.

This perennial species grows from a thickened rhizome with tooth-like projections. Three sheaths usually enclose the flowering stem. The otherwise naked stem is 2–12 inches (5–35 cm) high, pale yellow-green or brownish red with 2–18 reflexed flowers in a loose raceme $^{1}/_{2}$–3 inches (1.2–5 cm) long. The sepals and petals are purple-brown and much alike, joining to form a short hood over the lip. The lip is $^{1}/_{16}$ – $^{1}/_{8}$ inch (2–3 mm) long and white with magenta-purple markings. It

86

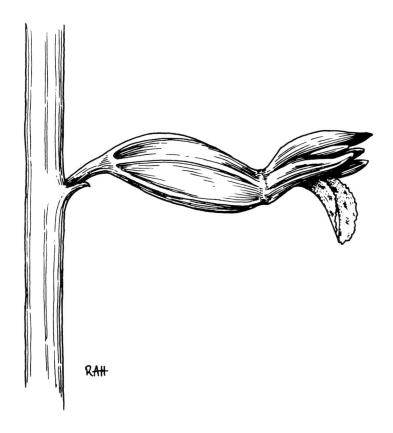

is reflexed with flaring, crinkled or occasionally shallowly toothed edges.

This is one of the smallest-flowered orchids in Missouri. The tiny flowers of this species are comparable in size to *Spiranthes tuberosa* and *Malaxis unifolia*.

Technical Description:

Perennials; scapes from thickened rhizomes with toothlike projections, 5–35 cm high, pale yellow-green or purple-brown; raceme 2–20 flowered, 1–8 cm long; perianth 2.5–4 mm long, ovaries globose, yellow-green, on slender pedicels; sepals and petals similar, linear lanceolate, joined to form short hood; lip 2–3 mm long, white with purple markings, margins crinkled or shallow-toothed; capsules globose, 3–7 mm long.

2. *Corallorhiza wisteriana* Conrad

Named for its discoverer, Charles J. Wister, 1782–1865

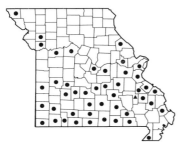

Common Name: Early coral root

Flowers April through May, rarely September

Early coral root occurs in rich or rocky acid soils of low wooded valleys, ravine bottoms, along streams and on ridges and slopes of open woods. It occurs throughout the Ozark and Ozark Border divisions and infrequently elsewhere.

The naked flowering stem grows from thickened rhizomes to about 15 inches (35 cm) in height. It has colorless sheaths replacing leaves on the lower portion and is purple-brown, purple-red or purple. The stem ends with a loose raceme of short-stalked flowers. The sepals and petals (tepals) are linear, similar in appearance, and join to form a hood over the lip. The sepals are purple-brown, dashed with darker

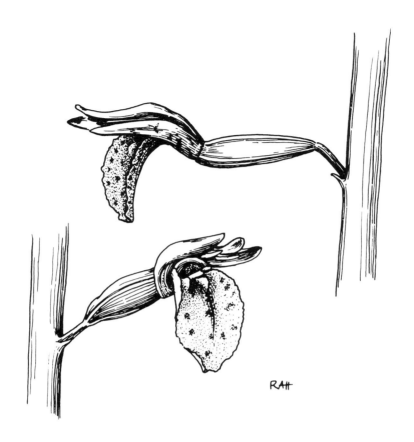

lines. The petals are paler and flecked with purple. The lip arches downward and is white with magenta-purple markings. The anther column can be seen through the opening above the lip, arching up under the hood.

This species, like other coral roots, tends to be colonial, with colonies consisting of a dozen or more plants.

Technical Description:
Coarse, 10–45 cm high; scape bulbous at base, from small rhizome, red or purple with pale sheaths below; raceme open, 2–13 cm long; flowers horizontal becoming reflexed; perianth 6–8 mm long; sepals linear, somewhat spreading, reddish or purplish backed, paler inner surfaces flecked with purple; petals purple-flecked, shorter and broader; lip 5 mm long, reflexed, roundish with basal claw, white with purplish dots, emarginate; capsules 8–12 mm long.

MALAXIS Sw.

Adder's mouth

Malaxis comes from *malacos*, "weak" or "delicate," in reference to the fragile nature of some members of the genus.

Malaxis unifolia Michx.

The specific name means "one-leafed."

Synonymy: *Malaxis ophioglossoides* Muhl. ex Willd.
Microstylis ophioglossoides (Muhl.) Nutt.
Microstylis unifolia (Michx.) BSP.

Common Name: Adder's mouth orchid

Flowers late May to early July

This species is found in acid soils of wooded slopes or ridges and along ravine bottoms and valley floors. It is rare and scattered in the Ozark and Ozark Border divisions.

The tiny adder's mouth orchid seldom grows any taller than 6 inches (15 cm). The stem grows from a solid, thickened root or tuber, with a solitary leaf clasping the stem about midway. The leaf is oval and oblong or broadly elliptic. Rarely, a second leaf occurs above the usual one, although this form has not been reported from Missouri. The stem ends with a cluster (raceme) of very tiny greenish flowers. The lower sepals are oval in shape and spreading. The upper sepal is oblong to linear in shape. The petals are threadlike and reflexed. Both sepals and petals are only about $^1/_{16}$–$^1/_8$ inch (1–3 mm) long. Beneath each flower is a diminutive floral bract that remains green for a short while after the flowers have wilted.

Technical Description:

Low perennial from solid tuber; single stem 6–16 cm high; solitary leaf midway on stem, leaf oval, oblong or broadly elliptic, 3–8 cm long, 1.5–4.5 cm broad; raceme oblong-cylindric, 1–8 cm long, 1–2.5 cm thick, unexpanded summit truncate or conical; pedicels 4–10 mm long, divergent; flowers greenish; sepals 1–3 mm long, linear-oblong, lower 2 spreading, upper erect; petals 1–3 mm long, threadlike, reflexed; lip 2-lobed, 1.5–3 mm long; capsules 3–4 mm broad, few.

LIPARIS L.C. Rich.

Twayblade

Liparis is from the Greek *liparos*, "fat" or "shiny," referring to the succulent leaves.

Twayblades are low-growing perennials of woodlands and fens (calcareous wet meadows), characterized by a pair of broad basal leaves. The short, angled flowering stem ends in a few-flowered raceme.

There are 2 species of *Liparis* in Missouri, one common and the other quite rare. They are not difficult to separate. *Liparis liliifolia* is common throughout the state and is usually found in woodlands. Its leaves are quite broad and lie low to the ground in a slightly upright position. The flowers are brownish purple. *Liparis loeselii* is rare and found in fens. Its leaves are less broad and more upright than *L. liliifolia*, and the flowers are yellow-green.

Both species grow from corms. These underground stems form offshoots that develop into new plants. Small, single-leafed plants may often be found growing near larger parent plants.

Key to the Species

A. Flowers brownish purple, lip 7–12 mm; plants of wooded slopes, common throughout the state . . . . **1.** *L. liliifolia*, p. 93

A. Flowers yellow-green, lip 4–5 mm; plants of fens (calcareous wet meadows) and sinkhole pond margins, rare . . . **2.** *L. loeselii*, p. 95

1. *Liparis liliifolia* (L.) L.C. Rich. ex Lindl.

Liliifolia refers to the resemblance of the leaves to those of some lilies. It has been spelled *lilifolia* in some older books.

Synonymy: *Ophrys liliifolia* L.

Common Names: Large twayblade, lily twayblade, purple sutcheon

Flowers late May through June

This orchid grows in acid soils of rocky or non-rocky woods, along streams, on slopes and ridgetops and on shaded sandstone ledges along creeks. This species is found in the northeastern counties of the Glaciated Plains, the Ozark Border and the central portion of the Ozark Division. Plants are smooth and dark, shiny green, ranging from 3–12 inches (7.5–30 cm) in height. Two broad basal leaves grow from a roundish underground stem (corm). The angled, naked stem ends with a raceme of 5–25 flowers on slender greenish purple stalks. The leaves are elliptical in shape, 2–6 inches (5–15 cm) long and 1 1/2–3 1/2 inches (3.5–9 cm) broad with a partial midrib at the base where they clasp the stem. The lip of the flower is translucent and pale purple with noticeable veining. The sepals are yellow green; the lower 2 support the lip. The lateral petals are madder-purple, threadlike and curved downward.

The anther column has a rounded base clasped by the lip. It is curved toward the lip with a beaklike projection over the pollen masses. A visiting insect passes under the column as it gathers nectar at the base of the flower, allowing the pollen masses to adhere to its head and back.

This species often is found growing in small groups of 2–10 plants occurring in a small circle. These are formed from the underground stems (corms) characteristic of the genus.

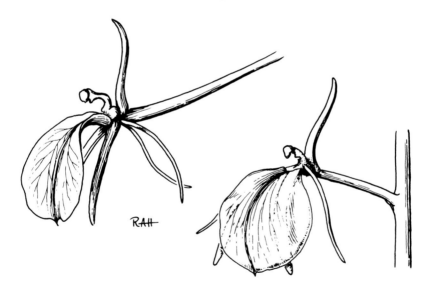

Technical Description:
Low perennials 6–30 cm high; roots solid bulbs or corms; leaves 2, basal, broadly elliptical to oval, glabrous, shining, 5–15 cm long, 3–9 cm broad, partial midrib at base; scape angled, glabrous; raceme 5–30

flowered; flowers pedicellate, pedicels 7–15 mm long; sepals yellow green, oblong-lanceolate, twisted, 10–12 mm long, 2–2.5 mm broad; lateral petals madder purple, threadlike, twisted, linear, 10–12 mm long; lip entire, broadly cuneate-obovate, translucent, madder-purple with noticeable veins, 7–12 mm long, 7–12 mm broad; capsules 1.5–1.8 cm long.

2. *Liparis loeselii* (L.) L.C. Rich.

Named for John Loesel, 1607–1655

Synonymy: *Ophrys loeselii* L.

Common Names: Loesel's twayblade, yellow twayblade

Flowers May to June

95

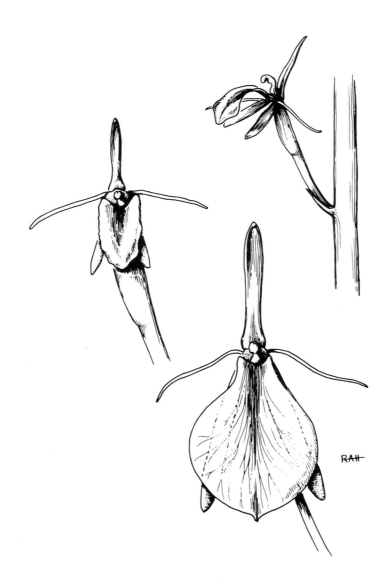

This species inhabits fens (calcareous wet meadows), alder thickets and margins of sinkhole ponds. In Missouri, it is known only from Bollinger, Butler, Carter, Madison, Shannon and Wayne counties in the southeastern part of the state, and from Laclede County in the Upper Ozark Section.

This species is smaller than *L. liliifolia*. The plants are 3–10 inches (7.5–25 cm) tall, with a pair of leaves clasping the flowering stem at ground level. The leaves are lance-shaped to long oval, about 6 inches (15 cm) long and light green in color. They are keeled and in an upright position on either side of the stem. The angled stem grows from a thickened underground stem (corm). It ends with a crowded raceme of yellow-green flowers. The sepals are narrowly oblong, and the lateral petals are linear in shape and twisted. The lip is oblong in shape and slightly turned up along the margin.

This orchid was first found in Missouri by Steyermark in 1936 in a calcareous wet meadow in Shannon County. Numerous attempts to find other locations for the species were unsuccessful until 1979, when 2 new sites were located. Father James Sullivan found several plants in a fen in Carter County on June 20, several weeks after Rebecca Haefner had found a population in Bollinger County along the margin of a sinkhole pond. Since that time, additional populations have been found in Butler, Laclede, Madison and Wayne counties.

At the Carter County location, the plants grow with grasses and sedges on a small tussock in a fen, where the dense grass cover makes the orchids difficult to find. The fen is bordered on one side by a spring branch along which grows a thicket of willows that shades the orchids from the afternoon sun. I counted 28 plants at the site, many of which had last year's seed pods standing next to them. Some associated plants included ragwort, Indian paintbrush, flax, ninebark, wood betony, swamp lousewort, lobelia, blue-eyed grass, dwarf St. John's-wort, spotted cowbane, swamp milkweed, buttonbush, boneset, the rare Ridell's goldenrod, and numerous grass and sedge species.

Technical Description:

Low perennials, 5–30 cm high; roots a solid, bulblike corm; leaves basal, paired, strongly keeled, lanceolate to lance-ovate, up to 15 cm long, light green; scape angled, terminated by a raceme of yellow-green flowers; flowers 2–25 on ascending pedicels, 5 mm broad; upper sepal with wide, expanded base, erect; lower sepals linear, supporting the lip; petals filiform, extended outward, horizontal to erect; lip oblong to obovate-spatulate, toothed at apex, with crystalline margins, 5 mm long; capsules longer than pedicels.

APLECTRUM Torr.

Adam-and-Eve orchid

The name comes from the prefix *a*, "without," and the Greek *plectron*, "spur."

Aplectrum hyemale (Muhl. ex Willd.) Torr.

Hyemale, "of winter," refers to the overwintering nature of the leaf.

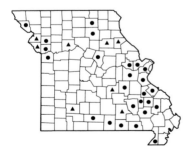

Synonymy: *Cymbidium hyemale* Muhl. ex Willd.

Common Names: Adam-and-Eve orchid, putty root

Flowers mid-May to early June

98

This species occurs in low, rich woods, along streams and in ravine bottoms. It is known from the Ozark Border and Ozark divisions, and also has been reported from Buchanan, Jackson, Clinton and Greene counties, to the south and west.

The plants of this species grow up to 20 inches (50 cm) tall. The solitary, leafless stems arise from solid underground stems called corms. Each corm usually lasts only 2 years. Several corms may be connected by a slender branch, forming a chain. In autumn, the corm sends up a single evergreen leaf. The leaf is elliptical in shape and may grow up to 8 inches (20 cm) long and 3 1/2 inches (9 cm) wide. It is blue-green or dark green and strongly ribbed or pleated. The leaf usually withers by early May.

A single flowering stem emerges in mid-May as the leaf withers. The raceme is 6 – 8 inches (15 – 20 cm) long and bears 8 – 20 yellowish purple flowers. The flowers are about 1/2 inch (12 mm) long. The sepals and petals are similar in appearance and oblong in shape with the petals being slightly shorter than the sepals. The 3-lobed lip is white with magenta markings. The middle lobe is longest and has wavy margins.

The name Adam and Eve comes from the method of vegetative reproduction in the species by which the rootstock produces a new corm each year connected to the old one by a slender branch. The corms contain a glutinous substance that once was used as an adhesive to mend broken pottery. Hence the other common name, putty root.

Technical description:
Rootstocks with biennial corms 1–2.5 cm broad, 2–4 corms often connected by narrow strands; leaf solitary, basal, elliptic, 7–20 cm long, 4–9 cm broad, overwintering, corrugate striate, withering at flowering time; scape stout yellow-green, 30–50 cm high; raceme 15–20 cm long; flowers 8–20, 1 cm long; sepals and petals similar, yellow to yellow-green at base, becoming purple at apex, the upper sepal and upper petals forming a hood; lip 3-lobed, center lobe corrugate, white marked with magenta; capsules elliptic, reflexed, 1.5–2.5 cm long, 5–10 mm broad.

TIPULARIA Nuttall

Cranefly Orchid

The botanical name *Tipularia* is from the Latin *tipula,* "waterspider," from the genus of insects to which craneflies belong. The flowers resemble craneflies resting on an upright stem.

Tipularia discolor (Pursh) Nutt.

From the Latin *discolor,* "different colors faded," in reference to the dull colors of the flowers.

Synonymy: *Orchis discolor* Pursh
          Limodorum unifolium Muhl.
          Tipularia unifolia (Muhl.) BSP.

Common Name: Cranefly orchid

Flowers July to August

This species was first collected in the state in 1988 by Mark Pelton from sand dunes in seasonally wet bottomland forest of the Mississippi Lowlands Division in Butler County. With expanded searches, it has been recorded in Oregon and Stoddard counties as well. In Stoddard County, it occurs at the base of Crowley's Ridge in a beech, tulip poplar and sweet gum forest, where the ridge meets the Mississippi Lowlands. Many plants occur singly or several in small colonies scattered along low terraces bordering a small, spring-fed stream. The rich sandy soil is covered by moderate leaf cover with very little competing vegetation.

The Oregon County site, located in the Ozark Natural Division, is a low, wooded terrace dominated by eastern red cedar bordering a running stream. The site at one time appeared to be a small field, but it now is invaded by oak, hickory and cedar. One colony of four plants was observed in rather dry, rocky and sandy, acid soil shaded by cedar.

The plants of this species grow up to 18 inches (45 cm) tall. The solitary, leafless stem arises from solid underground stems called corms. Several corms may be connected. In autumn each corm sends up a single overwintering leaf. The leaf is ovate in shape and may grow to 4 inches (10 cm) long and 2 ½ inches (6 cm) wide. It is dark green, with small scattered purple spots on the upper surface, and the lower surface is wine-purple. The leaf usually withers by May.

A single flowering stem emerges in early July after the leaf has withered. The raceme occupying the upper half of the scape bears about 30 light purple-green or gray flowers. The flowers are about $1/3$ inch (8 mm) long. The petals and sepals are similar in appearance, oblong-elliptic, up to $1/5$ inch (5 mm) long. The 3-lobed lip has small, rounded lateral lobes, and the middle lobe is long, narrow, and spreading somewhat at the tip. It is up to $1/3$ inch (8 mm) long. The slender spur is about $3/4$ inch (18 mm) long. Where dozens of leaves are seen in winter, only a few flowering stems may be seen in summer.

The flowering scapes are difficult to see in the dappled sunlight of the forest floor. I have been more successful in looking for new sites during the winter, when the colonies of dark green leaves are more easily visible laying on top of the surrounding brown leaf cover and when more light reaches the forest floor.

Technical Description:
Rootstock fleshy, in a jointed series of 2–3 corms, 10–15 mm long, 6–10 mm wide; leaf solitary, ovate 6–10 cm long, 4–6 cm wide, dark green above with small purple spots, wine purple below, present autumn to spring; scape slender purplish brown 30–45 cm tall; raceme 12–20 cm long; flowers 25–40, 8 mm long, light purple-green, or gray; sepals and petals similar, 5 mm long, spreading, pale purple, gray tinged with green; lip 3-lobed, lateral lobes rounded, small, middle lobe long and narrow spreading at the apex with a basal spur 13–18 mm long.

HEXALECTRIS Raf.

Crested coral root

The name probably comes from the Greek *hex*, "six," and *alectryon*, "cock," in reference to the cockscomb appearance of the crest on the lip.

Hexalectris spicata (Walt.) Barnh.

Synonymy: *Arethusa spicata* Walt.
Bletia aphylla Nutt.
Hexalectris aphylla (Nutt.) Raf.

Common Name: Crested coral root

Flowers mid-July to September

This species occurs in dry, rocky woods underlaid by limestone, along bluffs and bordering glades. It is found infrequently in the Ozark Border and Ozark divisions. The species reaches its northern range limit in Missouri.

A single stem up to 30 inches (90 cm) tall emerges from a sturdy ringlike rhizome with corallike projections. The stem is tan or brownish purple and stout, topped by a loose raceme of flowers. The leaves are reduced to purplish sheathing scales. The flowers are yellow to yellow-brown, striped with purple-brown. The 3-lobed lip is white with purple veining. The 2 lateral lobes turn up along the sides of the central lobe, which is longer and has several longitudinal ridges that form a crest. The flowers at the bottom of the raceme begin opening first. Mature, pollinated flowers do not drop off, but wither and remain attached. Flowers that are not pollinated do drop off the plant.

In fall and winter, the dried stalks and capsules of this species somewhat resemble those of the Adam-and-Eve orchid *(Aplectrum hyemale)*. The capsules of *H. spicata* differ in being obovoid with a broad, rounded end and are on short stalks. The capsules of *A. hyemale* are sessile and elliptical in shape.

Hexalectris, like the coral roots *(Corallorhiza),* is saprophytic. The plants lack any green color and derive their nourishment from mycorrhizal fungi associated with their roots, rather than from the sun.

Technical Description:
Plants leafless, 16–90 cm high, lacking green color; rootstocks with stout, annular rhizomes with projections; scape stout with bracts; flowers in racemes, 6–30 cm long; flowers 2 cm long, sepals and petals similar, oval, obtuse, somewhat spreading; lip 3-lobed with crested center.

References

Fernald, Merritt L. 1950. *Gray's Manual of Botany,* Eighth Edition. American Book Company, Chicago. 1632 pp.

Homoya, Michael A. 1993. *Orchids of Indiana,* Indiana Academy of Science, Indianapolis, Indiana. 276 pp.

Luer, Carlyle A. 1975. *The Native Orchids of the United States and Canada Excluding Florida.* New York Botanical Garden, The Bronx. 361 pp.

Magrath, Lawrence K., and James L. Norman. 1989. Nomenclatural notes on *Calopogon, Corallorhiza,* and *Cypripedium* (Orchidaceae) in the Great Plains region. *Sida* 13: 371-372.

Mohlenbrock, Robert H., ed. 1970, *The Illustrated Flora of Illinois: Flowering Plants – Lilies to Orchids.* Southern Illinois University Press, Carbondale. 288 pp.

Rickett, Harold W. 1966. *Wildflowers of the United States, the Northeastern States,* Volume 1, Part 1. McGraw-Hill Book Co., New York. 230 pp.

Sheviak, Charles J. 1973. "A new Spiranthes from the grasslands of central North America." Botanical Museum Leaflets 23: 285-297.

Sheviak, Charles J. 1974. *An Introduction to the Ecology of the Illinois Orchidaceae.* Scientific Papers XIV. Illinois State Museum, Springfield. 89 pp.

Sheviak, Charles J., and Marlin L. Bowles. 1986. The prairie fringed orchids: a pollinator isolated species pair. *Rhodora* 88: 267-290.

Slaughter, Carl R. 1993. *Wild Orchids of Arkansas.* Published by author. 100 pp.

Stevens, William C. 1961, *Kansas Wildflowers,* second edition. University of Kansas Press, Lawrence. 461 pp.

Steyermark, Julian A. 1963. *Flora of Missouri.* Iowa State University Press, Ames. 1725 pp.

Summers, Bill. 1987. *Missouri Orchids,* revised edition. Missouri Department of Conservation, Jefferson City. 92 pp.

Thom, Richard H., and James H. Wilson. 1980. The Natural Divisions of Missouri. *Transactions of the Missouri Academy of Sciences* 14:9-23.

Yatskievych, George, and Joanna Turner. 1990. Catalogue of the Flora of Missouri. *Monographs in Systematic Botany from The Missouri Botanical Garden* 37: i-xii, 1-345.

Glossary

A

acute: ending in a sharp angle or point

anthesis: period when a plant is in flower

attenuate: gradually becoming very narrow

B

basal: occurring around the base of the plant

bracteose: with numerous bracts

C

capsule: a dry fruit with more than one compartment

cauline: on the stem

clavate: club-shaped

column: in orchids, the united style and stamens

connivent: converging

corm: enlarged, fleshy, underground base of a stem

cuneate: wedge-shaped

D

dentate: toothed

E

erose: as if gnawed or chewed

F

falcate: curved and flat, like a scythe

flabellate: fan-shaped

G

galeate: helmet-shaped

glabrous: smooth, without hairs

I
inflorescence: cluster of flowers

K
keel: central dorsal ridge, as in a boat

L
lip: the prominent modified petal of orchid flowers, usually in the lowermost position

O
ovary: part of the flower containing the ovules

ovules: seeds-to-be

P
pedicel: stalk of a single flower

peduncle: flower stalk supporting either a cluster or a solitary flower

perennial: lasting year after year

perianth: the sepals and petals, collectively

petal: the usually bright-colored portion of the flower; the internal series of flower parts

petiole: leaf stalk

pistil: the female portion of the flower, consisting of the stigma, style (when present) and ovary

pollinium: a coherent mass of pollen

pubescent: covered with hairs

R
raceme: a type of inflorescence where the flowers are attached to the central axis on short stalks (pedicels)

rachis: the axis of an inflorescence

rhizome: a horizontal underground stem

S

scape: a leafless flowering stem

secund: directed to one side

sepal: the outer portion of the flower, often green, but in orchids usually similar to the lateral petals

sessile: without a stalk

spiciform: spikelike

spike: a type of inflorescence with the flowers' sessile on a common axis

spur: a hollow, tubular extension of some part of the flower, usually containing nectar; in orchids, the spur extends from the lip

stamen: the pollen-bearing portion of the flower

stigma: the part of the pistil that receives the pollen

stolon: a runner along the ground surface that may root

T

tepal: sepals and petals of similar form

tripartite: divided into three parts

truncate: ending abruptly as if cut off

tuber: a thickened underground branch having many buds or eyes, e.g., a potato

V

variety: a subdivision of a species

viscidium: the sticky body attached to the pollinium that connects it to the pollinator

Index